MINING
THE LOTHIANS

Two young miners from Vogrie, Midlothian.

Guthrie Hutton

Stenlake Publishing
1998

This book has been produced in association with
the Scottish Mining Museum, Lady Victoria colliery, Newtongrange.

by Stenlake Publishing
Telephone / Fax: 01290 551122

ISBN 1 84033 047 3

Miners queue in the snow for a bus outside Lady Victoria colliery, 1946.

INTRODUCTION

The story of mining in the Lothians is dominated by coal, although other minerals like clay, ironstone, lime and sandstone were also worked. The most conspicuous remains of mineral extraction are, however, the vast bings of spent shale that dominate the landscape of West Lothian and what was the south-west corner of Midlothian. They testify to the scale of the oil industry that flourished for over a hundred years from the 1850s.

Coal has been won in the Lothians for centuries. The monks of Newbattle Abbey are known to have been digging it in the thirteenth century and it seems likely that they, and others, worked it before then. They would have used it for domestic purposes and for firing kilns and salt pans.

After the Reformation and the dissolution of the monasteries, the big landowners took over. They developed the coal workings as commercial enterprises and in the seventeenth and early eighteenth centuries most of Scotland's coal came from around the Fife and Lothian coasts. Much of it was exported and the Forth became one of the busiest trading areas in the British Isles and a centre of the salt industry.

Coal workings and salt pans were dangerous and unpleasant places, and by the early seventeenth century it was proving difficult to recruit and retain people to work in them. Poaching of experienced men was rife. The Scottish Parliament, anxious to avoid disruption to such important industries, passed a law in 1606 to protect them. The Act effectively tied colliers and salters to their overlord, like serfs or slaves. It was extended in 1641 to include other essential workers. Men were regarded as part of the mine. They were unable to leave to find other work without the permission of their overlord, and since that was unlikely to be granted, they were stuck. If they left of their own accord they were deemed to have stolen themselves from their employer. The law remained unchallenged until 1775 when an attempt was made to amend it. It was repealed in 1799, but the legacy lingered long after in the minds of landowners and miners.

The forces that began to challenge the old law had their roots partly in West Lothian, where the rich mineral resources of Bo'ness led to the great Carron Ironworks being set up nearby. It went into blast in 1760 and started a shift of Scottish trade, commerce and industry to the west. Other ironworks followed – only a few at first, and some not very big – but towards the end of the century the pace and scale of industrial development quickened. The invention of hot blast smelting, and the use of blackband ironstone in the early 1830s, accelerated the growth of the Lanarkshire iron and coal industries. The need for thousands of miners was met by a wave of Irish immigration; cheap labour and market forces swept away any remnant of the master/slave relationship.

West Lothian was drawn into the Lanarkshire revolution, but in Mid- and East Lothian the old order held sway. Collieries were still part of the big estates, and although coal was used by industries like salt pans, potteries, breweries and glassworks, the coal-owners operated cartels to keep prices artificially high for export. Domestic customers were also cheated by carters who gave short measure, and so, despite having vast quantities of coal on its doorstep, Edinburgh suffered high prices and

Winding engineman, Willie Mitchell, walks past Emily Bank, Arniston in the early 1960s.

fuel shortages. The city's answer was to build the Union Canal to bring in coal from the west. Its opening in 1822 broke the cartels, but old attitudes lingered.

A Parliamentary Commission, set up in 1840, saw no women and children working in mines in the west, but found many being used to carry huge loads of coal out of the steep mines of Mid- and East Lothian. The further east the commissioners went, the worse it got. They likened the practice to a remnant of slavery and their damning report formed the basis of legislation in 1842 which outlawed women, girls and boys under ten from working underground.

Resistance in the Lothians was strong, but time was catching up on the old feudal order and by the mid-nineteenth century railways were opening up the coalfields away from the coasts. The big Lanarkshire companies, searching for new sources of coal and ironstone, also started to move in on the relatively unexploited Lothians. Family concerns could not match these aggressive entrepreneurs and one by one they were swallowed up or amalgamated with others to form local coal companies. Despite this expansion the industry in the Lothians remained small scale. In 1900, 56% of the Scottish industry was in Lanarkshire, while only 3% was in West Lothian and 5% in Mid- and East Lothian. But half a century and two world wars later, the Lanarkshire pits that had fuelled Scotland's industrial revolution were exhausted, the coal industry had been nationalised and the Lothians were set to become Scotland's coal counties again.

When the National Coal Board took over in 1947 the country was trying to recover from six years of war. Coal was desperately needed and the NCB looked for new areas to develop. Top of their list was the Esk Basin. As the industry moved east, mining families moved with it, and the small towns and villages of Midlothian suddenly grew with a large influx of people from the west. The County Council faced both a housing and a social problem. Instead of being able to plan and develop a diverse economy, the NCB thrust one-industry towns on them. New showpiece pits at Bilston Glen and Monktonhall were amongst nine new sinkings, thirty-eight reconstructions, and numerous shallow drift mines planned in the Lothians by the Coal Board. By 1953 output had increased by over half a million tons a year, 1,000 more men were employed and over 3,000 houses had been built for incoming miners and their families.

Initially the Coal Board could do no wrong, but by the late 1950s the honeymoon was over. Britain was emerging from its desperate post-war problems, oil and nuclear power were making inroads into coal's traditional markets, and smokeless zones were cutting domestic use. Demand was falling at a rate of 25 million tons a year and there was a glut of coal at pit-heads and power stations. Old uneconomic pits were shut to slow down the rate of production, but the NCB faced some hard choices when the big developments were ready to produce coal. More pits were closed and resources were concentrated on the new investments, but still demand fell and closure became an unremitting process, made worse by the discovery of oil and natural gas in the North Sea.

By the mid-1960s, East Lothian's pits had all shut and closures in Midlothian had cost 5,000 jobs. Through the 1970s Bilston Glen and Monktonhall kept output high, and the closures continued, until, by the time of the last great national strike in 1984, they were all that was left; in West Lothian only Polkemmet remained. They had all gone by the end of the decade.

Monktonhall burst briefly into life again in 1992 and survived for another five years in a brave but ultimately doomed attempt to revive a once proud industry.

Guthrie Hutton, 1998

Paul Robeson entertains miners in the canteen at Woolmet colliery in May 1949. The great singer and political activist was in Edinburgh at the invitation of the union, who had organised a special concert in the Usher Hall for miners and their families.

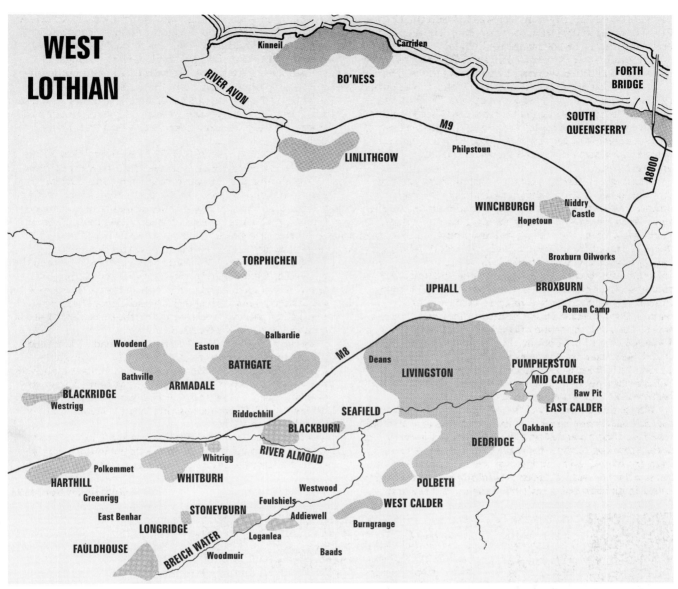

WEST LOTHIAN

Kinneil
Carriden
BO'NESS
RIVER AVON
FORTH BRIDGE
M9
SOUTH QUEENSFERRY
Philpstoun
LINLITHGOW
A8000
WINCHBURGH
Niddry Castle
Hopetoun
Broxburn Oilworks
TORPHICHEN
UPHALL
BROXBURN
Roman Camp
Woodend
Balbardie
Easton
Deans
PUMPHERSTON
BATHGATE
LIVINGSTON
MID CALDER
Bathville
M8
Raw Pit
Blackvville
ARMADALE
EAST CALDER
BLACKRIDGE
Oakbank
Westrigg
Riddochhill
SEAFIELD
BLACKBURN
DEDRIDGE
RIVER ALMOND
Whitrigg
Polkemmet
WHITBURH
Westwood
POLBETH
HARTHILL
Greenrigg
Foulshiels
WEST CALDER
East Benhar
STONEYBURN
Addiewell
Burngrange
LONGRIDGE
Loganlea
FAULDHOUSE
BREICH WATER
Woodmuir
Baads

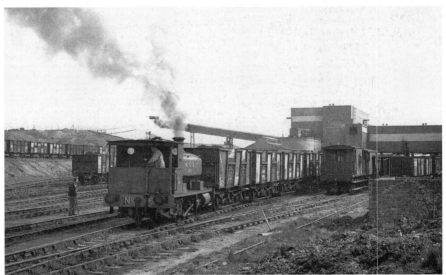

This 'pug' was built by one of Scotland's foremost makers of industrial steam locomotives, Andrew Barclay of Kilmarnock. She started life at United Collieries' Bathville works in 1937, but is seen here in the 1970s, near the end of her days, at the Kinneil preparation plant.

Kinneil was isolated geographically from the other West Lothian pits, and the National Coal Board kept it apart administratively. Initially it was part of the Fife and Clackmannan Area, then the Alloa Area when that was set up in 1951. When the five Scottish areas were reduced to two in 1967 it was the only Lothian pit in the North Area. Scotland was managed as one area from 1973.

Monks are known to have been working outcrop coal at Carriden at the end of the thirteenth century. They, and later private owners, continued to work both this coal and the shallower undersea seams until the entrepreneurs who set up the great Carron Ironworks arrived in the Bo'ness area in the late 1750s. One, Dr John Roebuck, developed considerable mining interests in the area and in 1769 invited James Watt to work on the development of an experimental steam engine to be applied to the mining industry. Sadly Roebuck's ebullient and adventurous spirit was not matched by financial acumen and his mining activities led to insolvency shortly afterwards. Watt, deprived of a patron, headed for Birmingham to continue his work and Scottish mining lost a major technological innovator.

Nevertheless mining in the Bo'ness area continued. The coal was of high coking quality and of great value to the iron industry. The Carriden pit was sunk by the Carriden Coal Company in 1914 and was taken over in the late 1930s by Baird's and Scottish Steel. By the early 1950s difficult working conditions had reduced output per man shift to less than a ton and it closed in 1954.

Coal came up from the pit along with a mixture of stone and dross which had to be removed. In later preparation plants much of the process was mechanised, but at older pits the stone was removed by hand at the picking tables. The pickers (above) were often female, as here at Carriden, and they plucked lumps of stone from the jigging conveyors as they passed in front of them. Strong fingers would have been needed to 'pick' some of the stones lying on this floor.

Numerous pits were sunk in the Kinneil area over the years including the extensive Furnaceyard colliery. It was operated by the Kinneil Cannel and Coking Coal Co. Ltd. initially on its own, but from 1926 as a subsidiary of the Lochgelly Iron and Coal Co. It went into liquidation in 1933, but continued in operation until the mid-1930s when an improvement in exports allowed the pit to run without a loss and avoid closure.

Just before nationalisation a new underground mine, dipping at 1 in 9, was driven north under the Forth from the Furnaceyard workings. It took twelve months to complete and went beyond a large fault to the previously untapped Seven Feet seam. By late 1946 large quantities of good quality coking coal were being won and double winding was being contemplated.

The NCB went further and put down bores beyond the Seven Feet seam. They found 40 feet of coal in twelve seams of between 7 feet 9 inches and 2 feet thickness, and planned a new Kinneil colliery to get at them. In June 1951 the Countess of Balfour, wife of the NCB's Scottish Divisional Chairman, cut the first sod for two new 22 foot diameter shafts. They were sunk in the existing Furnaceyard colliery yard and are seen here in the process of development.

The Coal Board sacrificed patriotism for speed when they ordered shaft sinking equipment from a German company who could supply it sooner than their British competitors. Despite the criticism, the Coal Board's decision was welcomed by the steel industry which urgently needed the new pit's coking coal.

With output less than half of what had been expected, the redeveloped Kinneil was rapidly gaining 'white elephant' status when a tunnel was driven under the Forth to link it with Valleyfield colliery in Fife. In April 1964, after eighteen months of tunnelling, stone drivers Martin 'Tiger' Shaw working from Kinneil, and Andrew Drysdale from Valleyfield, broke through the last sandstone barrier. The pit managers shook hands through the gap to mark an occasion of historic significance. It was also a moment of great pride for the mining communities: they could walk below the river estuary several months before people could drive across the new Forth Bridge. When the tunnel was

operational most of the output from the two pits was brought up to the new preparation plant at Kinneil. A locomotive hauled man-riding system was introduced in the early 1970s and a conveyor system installed to move materials and coal.

The tower for No. 1 shaft was equipped with four cages and electric winding. This picture from it looks past the more conventional headgear for No. 2 shaft towards Bo'ness. Despite Coal Board predictions in the 1950s that the pit would have a life of 100 years it closed in 1982 amidst threats of a major national strike.

Westrigg colliery, at Blackridge, was to the south of the Barbauchlaw Burn which put it on the Lanarkshire side of the old county boundary. The boundary has now shifted and the site of the old pit is in West Lothian. The Westcraigs miners' rows, which were always in West Lothian, can be seen in the background of this view looking north from the pit bing.

These men at Westrigg are unloading props, or 'trees' as miners called them. Many men preferred wooden props to the later hydraulic ones, because they creaked when the weight came on. Experienced men could tell from the sound when they were about to give way. Miners also liked wooden props because they had to be cut to size and all the little (and some not so little!) offcuts – 'clogs' – made excellent firewood.

Originally a seam of steam coal was worked close to the surface at Westrigg by a Mr Moir. When he died in 1888 the pit was taken over by Bathville coal-owner, James Wood, who extended and deepened the workings. He also built a bank of coke ovens at the pit-head – these furnaces could have been used to fire them. In 1902 United Collieries took over from James Wood. They worked the pit for a number of years, but it always operated near the margins and had to be closed on a number of occasions when losses became too high. Westrigg was shut down for the last time in 1930 although it was kept on as a pumping station. The neighbouring Blackrigg pit closed in 1955.

Blackridge became the site of one of the first opencast sites in Scotland when the NCB opened up an area near the village in the late 1960s. It worked anthracite, a fuel that was in short supply at the time and much needed because of the smokeless zones being introduced in towns and cities.

James Wood and Company built a number of miners' houses on the main Airdrie to Bathgate Road. This picture, taken by a Blackridge photographer, shows some miners' cottages being visited by the fish cart – fresh cod was a rare treat for people living far from the coast.

United Collieries Ltd. was set up in 1898 to amalgamate small coal companies and by 1902 had acquired over thirty, including the Armadale Coal Company and its Bathville Fireclay Works. The company later operated them under an associate company known as United Fireclay Products Ltd. It remained independent of the National Coal Board in 1947. Coal is the compressed, decayed remains of long dead trees that grew in primeval swamps; clay was formed from the beds of the swamps. There was a lot of it in the pits around Armadale where it was used by fireclay works to make bricks and a wide variety of products like drains, tiles and chimney cans.

This United Collieries' pug was built by Dick and Stevenson of Airdrie and appears to have operated between Westrigg colliery and the Bathville fireclay works. It was scrapped in 1938 while working at Bathville.

Woodend village near Armadale, where the Coltness Iron Company worked bituminous coal and anthracite at their Woodend pit.

Woodend was a very wet pit and it was perhaps fitting that the NCB experimented there with a system designed to lift coal from the pit bottom to the surface in a high pressure water pipe. The technique was known as hydraulic transportation and had exercised the minds of coal industry engineers for years. The pit was chosen because its anthracite was produced in small-sized lumps and the shaft was only 250 feet deep. The idea was to push the small lumps of coal into water flowing in a six inch pipe at a rate of 750 gallons a minute. The system, designed to deal with 60 tons an hour, was inaugurated in July 1955. Ten years later roof conditions in the pit were deteriorating as the face line advanced and it closed in July 1965. The picture shows the washery which was built in the 1930s and was retained after the pit's closure to treat open-cast coal.

Geologically, West Lothian was part of the Lanarkshire coalfield and the county's pits were included in the area covered by the Lanarkshire Coalowners' Association. The NCB perpetuated the link by placing West Lothian pits, with the exception of those at Bo'ness, in the Central East Area and running them from Shotts. This association with the declining Lanarkshire field can hardly have helped to set a positive tone for West Lothian pits, but mechanisation was introduced at some of them in an attempt to boost production.

Easton pit at Bathgate, on the right in the background of this early 1950s view, was one of the county's most successful units. At one time Bathgate railway yard served over forty pits and was one of the largest in Scotland. Within twenty years of this picture being taken it was serving none.

Easton was linked to the older Balbardie pit which tapped the rising seams to the north of the town. The colliery was being worked by Walker and Cameron in 1895 when two of its six boilers burst, killing two men and injuring a third. The blast threw metal fragments weighing several tons for hundreds of yards and demolished the chimney. With all steam power lost the men underground had to escape through an adjacent mine. Failure of the brick supports, causing one of the boilers to buckle, was blamed. Two egg-end boilers, similar to the ones that exploded, can be seen in this picture. Balbardie was latterly used as a training pit and as a ventilation and escape shaft for Easton.

B.8316.

Easton's principal seam was the Wilsontown Main. It was between 5 and 8 feet thick, but had bands of dirt and stone up to 18 inches thick running through it. It was impossible to completely separate these, and large quantities of stone, dirt and bits of coal ended up on the enormous bings. They were continually on fire. In an attempt to damp them down, the pit water was pumped onto the bing but the fires turned the water to steam. The pit was due west of Bathgate and the bing's sulphurous fumes were borne by the prevailing winds across the town. When it rained, a weak sulphuric acid fell on roofs and trees, to the detriment of both.

A measure of the extent to which Bathgate's industry was centred around mining can be seen in these advertisements for the North British Steel Foundry. The cage, with a simple bowed steel plate roof and open sides, is typical of the kind of contraption that men trusted their lives to in the hazardous and uncomfortable industry of the late nineteenth and early twentieth centuries.

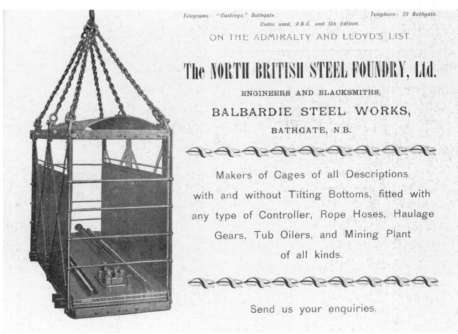

Opposite: Sinking at Easton, known originally as Hopetoun colliery, was begun in 1896 and coal was reached at just over 1,000 feet two years later. The pit was sunk by the Balbardie Colliery Company, who had taken over from Walker and Cameron. They in turn were taken over in 1907 by William Baird and Company (Baird's and Scottish Steel from 1939), one of the giants of the Lanarkshire coal and iron industries. In the 1950s the NCB electrified the winding engine and constructed a new washery.

In 1962 the NCB categorised pits according to their future prospects: category 'A' was for pits with prospects, if reserves were realised; 'B' pits had reserves, but an uncertain future; those with a 'C' rating had little or no future. Easton was category 'A'. It was still an 'A' at the next review in 1965 and the following year was given an 'unlimited' life of 15-20 years(!). Within four years, however, extensive faulting of the field made machine mining impractical and the pit closed in July 1973.

The upper picture shows a man-riding bogie train with a well supported roof above it – Easton was noted for bad roof conditions. The lower picture shows men being pulled up a steep dook by an endless rope man-haulage system. It helped the legs a bit, but was tough on the arms!

Riddochhill pit, between Bathgate and Blackburn, was sunk about 1888 and worked alongside the Mosside and Boghead pits by local coal-owner Gavin Paul and Sons. It was taken over in 1922 by William Baird & Co. who expanded and deepened the workings.

The NCB tried to give it a new lease of life through mechanisation, installing the first Joy continuous miner in Scotland in the Wilsontown Main coal seam in 1955. The machine, made in Greenock to an American design, was developed to produce maximum output from minimum face room without drilling or blasting. Six chains with tungsten carbide cutter picks made up a ripping head which was advanced into the coal by a three man crew. The coal was dropped at the back of the machine and loaded onto conveyors. The Joy miner was used to drive headings to the pit's boundary and the remaining coal was taken out by retreat mining, a process in which miners work back towards the shaft rather than out from it. Skip winding also replaced winding coal in hutches.

Riddochhill's Lady Morton Jewel coal was excellent and the Coal Board put the pit into their 'A' category in 1962 and again in 1965, but on St Andrew's Day 1968 it was closed. Shortly afterwards, the M8 motorway was driven through the conveniently vacant site. The abandoned pit was used as a source of water for the British Motor Corporation's truck plant at Bathgate.

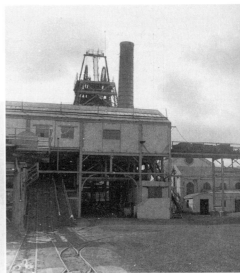

Robert Forrester & Co. worked the Whitrigg pit at East Whitburn from about 1900. When the NCB took it over they concentrated operations on the main No. 5 shaft which was also known as the Lady or Dales pit. It was 1,064 feet deep. No. 4, a 1 in 6 drift mine known as Burnbrae, was kept for ventilation and pumping and No. 6, the Latch, was also used for ventilation and as a means of egress. The pit worked the Lady Morton Jewel and Wilsontown Main coal and, as usual, the bing burned. When the wind was in the wrong direction the fumes could be drawn down No. 5 shaft by the ventilation system and the pit had to be shut.

Like its neighbours, Whitrigg had a reputation for poor industrial relations; the amount of jam on the rolls in the canteen could cause a strike. The NCB placed it in their 'A' category in 1962, but downgraded it to category 'C' in 1965 and listed it for closure. It was subsequently reprieved and reinstated as 'A' category but, when the Whitdale to Dechmont section of the M8 motorway was built in 1969, it cut the branch railway line that served Whitrigg and started a process of piecemeal closure. The washer was abandoned and the output taken by road to Easton and Polkemmet for treatment. The pit itself was closed in June 1972.

The whorls, the great pulley wheels that top the headframes, are seen here being hoisted onto the pit-head gantries at Polkemmet colliery.

Coal had been won on the Polkemmet Muir, near Whitburn, for decades, perhaps centuries, before one of Scotland's largest coal companies, William Dixon & Co., started sinking their new colliery just before the outbreak of the First World War. The second shaft was begun in 1916, but had to be stopped because of wartime restrictions. Dixon's tried to have the shaft sinkers exempted from conscription when it was introduced, but failed because the pit was not producing coal. Sinking Polkemmet was therefore a bit of a battle and its nickname, 'the Dardanelles', reflected another more terrible battle that was raging at the time. The flooded, incomplete shafts were pumped out and sinking to about 1,575 feet was restarted in 1921.

Polkemmet produced a high quality coking coal from the Wilsontown Main seam and also worked the Lady Morton Jewel coal. Reserves were extensive and exploration in the Fauldhouse area in 1975 proved a further 3.3 million tons. This picture shows No. 1 shaft, closest to camera. It was clad in concrete so that the ventilation could work at maximum efficiency. Without being enclosed the fan would simply draw air from the immediate area and not extract it from the pit. The shaft used to draw air out of the pit was known as the upcast, the air went in by way of the downcast shaft.

The baths are on the extreme right of this picture. They were opened in February 1937 and, at the time, were the second largest in Scotland to be built under the auspices of the Miners' Welfare Scheme. The site was gifted by Sir Adrian Baillie of Polkemmet, and the architect, J.J. Dempster, designed a classic 1930s building on a new layout. It had a central core with a glazed bow frontage, flanked by wings each containing 1,500 lockers for clean and dirty clothes. There were boot cleaners, boot greasing machines, taps with drinking water, a canteen and an ambulance and first aid room. The lum could be seen smoking for miles around because of Polkemmet's elevated location. It was demolished in November 1970 when the pit went electric.

This picture shows two Andrew Barclay locomotives leaving for Fauldhouse in 1978. Heavy trains had to be worked as double-headers like this to cope with the gradient past Greenrigg and East Benhar collieries, which were also served by the line. British Rail diesels took over from the pugs latterly.

Opposite: Polkemmet had a reputation for poor industrial relations before the NCB took over, and industrial unrest continued after nationalisation. When pits were classified according to their future prospects in 1962 Polkemmet was in category 'A', but after continued difficulties, below average output and lost money, it was downgraded to category 'B', 'with uncertain prospects'. It was restored to category 'A' in 1965, but unrest continued. During the national strike of 1984 the workings filled with water. They were pumped out when the strike ended but Polkemmet never reopened.

Polkemmet was at the end of a three-and-a-half mile long mineral railway that snaked across the moors from the Glasgow Central to Edinburgh railway at Fauldhouse. The line was worked by a group of pugs, two of which are seen here heading out of the colliery.

A pugs' graveyard outside the Polkemmet locomotive shed where the forlorn remains of a couple of locomotives lie at the side of the tracks.

A shotfirer and two machinemen pose beside an old coal-cutter at Greenrigg colliery near Harthill. The pit, owned by the Loganlea Coal Co., was taken over by United Collieries in 1902. Greenrigg produced coal and clay. Pit clay was rock hard and had to be removed as part of the pit-redd ('redd' means 'to clear up' in old Scots). Instead of being dumped on the waste bing, as happened at many collieries, Greenrigg's clay went to the brickworks at Bathville to make the 'Etna' brand of common bricks.

A pit-head fire at Greenrigg in 1924 destroyed all of the surface fitments except the new washer, offices, stores and workshops. Smoke pouring into the workings alerted the men to the problem, but with the headframes destroyed they had to escape through a connecting passage to Southrigg colliery near Shotts. The ponies were unable to get through the narrow gap and had to be led to another part of the pit to escape the fumes. The pit was reconstructed and continued in operation until 1960.

The Benhar Coal Co. developed coal workings on the moorland at East Benhar in the 1860s. Within thirty years the pit village had grown from nothing to 180 houses and a population of over 700. Both pit and village were taken over by Barr and Thornton in 1906; this picture of Castle Row dates from about that time. By 1929 the colliery was not working and the company had no interest in maintaining the village. It became derelict and insanitary and in 1932 the council decided to evacuate the population to new houses in Fauldhouse. A new East Benhar mine was opened in 1940, but with difficult geological conditions, and output halved since nationalisation, the first section of the mine was closed in October 1956 and the rest nine months later.

Fauldhouse became an identifiable community in the 1870s when the expansion of the mining industry caused a number of separate hamlets to merge into a single village. There were once numerous pits, but by the time of nationalisation all of them had closed. This picture is believed to show Braehead colliery, which was abandoned in March 1944. Its owners, Barr and Thornton, were the last mining company to work the Fauldhouse area.

Fauldhouse No. 1 colliery, where this pay packet was issued, was also known as the Knowes. It was one of many pits on the high moors around Shotts and Fauldhouse that were warned, immediately after the Second World War, to reduce strikes and improve output or face closure. Some took heed, but at Fauldhouse the warnings were ignored. A strike in January 1946 was followed a month later by a dispute over brushers' wages. The Ministry of Fuel and Power's regional controller issued a final notice. A month later sixteen strippers and drawers walked out, blaming bad ventilation. The Ministry's Inspectorate declared the complaint invalid, but the men went on strike again the following day and the pit was closed.

There was an outcry. Questions were asked in the House of Commons and a deputation went to London to lobby the Minister, Emmanuel Shinwell. He was 'unavailable', so they met his deputy, and the pit stayed closed. It continued to have a life of sorts as a pumping station for the Shotts pits and was also used for a few years as a training pit, but it has an unenviable place in history; closed by the Government before the NCB took over.

Name..... *Joe Colquhoun* 14

No......... Pay ending........... 19......

FAULDHOUSE COLLIERY.
BARR & THORNTON, Ltd.

		Rate.	£	S.	D.
Tons Coal, ...	...				
Tons Ironstone,	...				
Fathoms, 6	...	9/-	2	18	6
Days,	...	9			
....	...				

Offtakes.		£	S.	D.			
Cash, ...	...						
House Rent ...			10	4			
Coal, ...	...						
Smith ...	...						
Doctor, ...	...			5			
Nurse ...	...			2			
Checkweigher ...							
Explosives, ...							
Infirmary, ...				2			
Health Insur. ...				10			
Unem. Insur. ...				9			
Welfare Fund, ...				1			
Miners Home ...				1			
Subscription ...							
Holiday Fund ...					12	10	
.... 19				2	5	8	

The football team was part of the social fabric of a mining community and the game was often seen by young men as a passport to another, perhaps better way of life. Two members of the highly successful Fauldhouse United team of 1944/45 were signed by senior clubs. In that season, the club was accepted into the Lanarkshire and Lothians League and won everything: the league flag, the Lanarkshire Cup and the East of Scotland Cup. The following season they did even better, winning 45 consecutive games and five honours, including the Scottish Junior Cup. They are seen here celebrating their 2-0 final victory over Arthurlie at Hampden Park.

Boxing is another sport popular with miners and one of the most successful fighters from a Scottish mining community was Johnny Smillie of Fauldhouse. He was twice Amateur Boxing Association flyweight champion and was picked as the reserve for the British Olympic team at Helsinki in 1952. Two years later, boxing at bantamweight, he won a gold medal for Scotland at the Empire Games in Vancouver. He later turned professional and fought for the British bantamweight title.

Cricket is not commonly associated with mining communities, but the Fauldhouse Victoria Cricket Club is proof that in this corner of West Lothian it was once a very popular sport. The club was formed in 1855, some years before football became the universal game. It is thought to take its name from the Victoria pit at Crofthead. The club's origins are obscure. Suggestions that it may have been set up by English miners seem plausible, but the fact that neighbouring villages like Benhar, Breich and Harthill also had teams may simply mean that the game was more popular in Scotland at that time. A local farmer gifted the club their Eastfield ground in 1900 and, after ground preparations, the first home game was played in 1902. This is the 1903 team. Early matches were played against local teams which have now mostly disappeared, but Fauldhouse, with the advantage of having its own ground, went on to play in Scotland's senior leagues and became one of the country's most respected clubs.

Johnny Clark played as an all-rounder with Fauldhouse for fourteen years and was one of the club's finest players. He was a miner from Polkemmet and on match days someone with a car waited to collect him after his shift and take him to the game. On one such occasion, in a match against Hamilton Crescent (West of Scotland) in 1957, he scored 106 runs in 28 minutes. In another match he took all ten wickets in an innings.

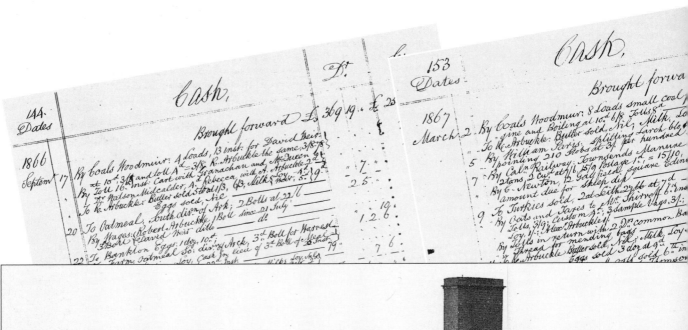

Woodmuir Colliery Company opened their pit at Breich in 1896, although as these entries from an estate ledger show, coal had been won at Woodmuir for many years before that. The company was acquired by United Collieries in 1902 and the pit worked in conjunction with their Loganlea and Foulshiels pits near Stoneyburn. It was nicknamed the Blinky; apparently a reference to the size of the village – if you blinked you missed it! When the NCB classified its pits in 1962, Woodmuir was in the lowest class – 'C' – those where reserves would be exhausted within five years. Even that gloomy prediction proved optimistic and Woodmuir was closed the following year, on the last working day before the annual summer holiday.

A local tramp used to frequent the pit's smithy for his Sunday breakfast. He would arrive, borrow a shovel and fry some ham and eggs on it over the fire.

The enclosed shaft behind the young men here at Loganlea No. 2 pit was the exception to the normal rule of having a ventilation fan draw air through the workings. At Loganlea a forcing fan pushed the air to upcast shafts at Foulshiels and Woodmuir collieries. The icy blast being driven into the pit in winter could make working conditions very uncomfortable and the pit bottomers had to wear layers of clothes, and scarves round their mouths, to keep warm. Miners often referred to upcast and downcast shafts as warm and cold pits. Forcing fans had some advantages. They increased air pressure on the coal face, hindering the escape of methane (firedamp), and propelled carbon dioxide (blackdamp) out of old workings and away from working faces and airways.

A new power house, built in 1891, made Loganlea one of the first collieries in Scotland to have electrically-powered haulages, drilling, coal-cutting and lighting. The pit, known locally as the Dykes, was declared uneconomic and closed in 1959, although some areas had been shut down ten years earlier.

Loganlea's ventilation fan and winding engine were driven by steam and this cooling pond was alongside the boiler house. Hot water was sprayed into the air to cool it and it made the pond lovely and warm – 'sheer joy' to the local youngsters who learned to swim in it. They were chased of course, but that clearly did not bother these water weans.

Baads mine was opened in 1905 by Young's Paraffin Light and Mineral Oil Company to supply their Pumpherston oil-works with coal. At the time of nationalisation it was being operated by Scottish Oils and they continued to work it for a while after vesting day. When the NCB took over, they continued to use it to provide fuel to the Pumpherston works. It was merged with the new Cuthill mine in 1961, but closed a year later when the oil-works was closed down. The mine was unofficially known as West Mains after the adjacent farm. A miner's explanation of the curious double 'aa' in the name was ' . . . because the mine was sunk by a man called Lamb'!

The Scottish coalfields were worked by men of many nationalities; these four of Scottish, Irish, Lithuanian and Polish descent are driving Cuthill mine near Stoneyburn in the 1950s. Cuthill was one of a number of small drift mines opened in the early years of the NCB. They were expected to show a quick return in coal and cash, but were also intended to employ men displaced from old pits, like Foulshiels and Loganlea, and keep them in work until the bigger developments were ready to absorb them. Cuthill was driven to a seam of Hurlet coal and opened in 1957. It was troubled by numerous faults and was not a success. It was linked underground with Baads in an attempt to make it easier to work, but it continued to struggle and the two mines were closed together.

This cheery looking lady in her pit clothes and 'peenie' is Sarah Thomson. She worked at the picking tables at Loganlea colliery and is believed to have been the last female coal worker employed by the National Coal Board in Scotland. Women took on surface work after they were banned from working underground by the Act of 1842.

One of the most redoubtable women of the Lothian mining communities was Sarah 'Ma' Moore JP. As an early Labour Party activist she was acquainted with Keir Hardie and other pioneers of the labour movement. She was Midlothian County Councillor for Addiewell, when, during the miners' strike of 1926, a local official took it upon himself to withhold money from the strikers. Ma was informed. She mobilised the women of the area who blockaded the West Calder Council office. The police were called, but when the 'riot' turned out to be women sitting on a doorstep, they were confused. They regained confidence when some men arrived and tipped over the official's car. A fight ensued, but Ma gave them all a verbal clip on the ear and sent them home. After a successful negotiation the 'siege' was raised and the victorious 'army' marched off singing 'It's a long way to Tipperaray'. Ma is seen here marshalling her troops.

SHALE OIL

James Young was a Glasgow born and educated chemist. He was working in Manchester when he first experimented with making oil from a spring of naphtha found in a Derbyshire coal mine. It ran dry in a couple of years, but Young believed it had been made by a natural distillation process and moved back to Scotland to experiment with distilling oil from coal. The best results came from Boghead Parrot, a cannel coal found at Torbanehill near Bathgate – 'cannel', because it burned with a bright flame like a candle; 'Parrot', because it crackled when it burned. It was also known as Torbaneite. Young took out a patent on his distillation process in 1850 and set up the world's first commercial refinery at Bathgate. The oil and paraffin wax it produced revolutionised domestic lighting and the good folk of Bathgate were the first to enjoy the benefits. Others tried to jump onto Young's bandwagon and he had to defend his patent in the courts. He travelled widely to collect his royalties, even to the USA.

Supplies of Boghead Parrot were limited and with extraction costs high and getting higher Young searched for another mineral. He 'found' shale in the Calders area, took out mineral leases and in 1866 opened the Addiewell oil-works. He was now a wealthy man at the head of a limited company – Young's Paraffin Light and Mineral Oil Co. Ltd. – and had also acquired a nickname – 'Paraffin' Young.

Shale is a hard sedimentary rock like compressed, solidified mud. It was found in workable seams in the Lothians stretching south in a broad band from the Forth estuary through Winchburgh, Broxburn and the Calders, ending up across the Lanarkshire county boundary at Tarbrax. The rock was usually worked from drift mines. It was baked in huge retorts to extract crude oil which was further distilled or refined and used to make a variety of products like paraffin, candles and petrol.

When first opened, Addiewell oil-works was the largest in the world. By the time the upper picture was taken early in the twentieth century, it covered 75 acres. By the 1920s competition from other fuels was creating problems and the candle-works closed in 1923, although production of crude oil, naphtha and ammonium sulphate continued until 1956. Young's original works at Bathgate, which had been operated for many years as an acid works, also closed in 1956.

In 1900 Addiewell works was retorting 4,200 tons of shale a week leaving, typically, 80% of spent shale or over 3,000 tons of waste. The works, operating for ninety years, produced an enormous bing which is seen here about to engulf a farm steading known as Bridgend or Clash-me-Doon.

The first new shale mining development for many years was Burngrange Nos. 1 and 2 pits, sunk at West Calder by Scottish Oils in the mid-1930s. The brick lined circular shafts went down over 400 feet to the 8 foot thick Dunnet seam which dipped at an angle of about 1 in 4. The pit was the scene of the worst disaster in the history of the shale mining industry, when an explosion on 10th January 1947 claimed fifteen lives.

The faceman inspecting the working area in the evening found the tops of the wooden props broken. He called to his drawer to look at them but as he approached, the flame on his carbide cap lamp ignited some gas. A plume of flame spread across the roof into old waste workings where an accumulation of undetected gas exploded. Men were blown off their feet. One was killed.

Although the explosion was heard at the pit-head fourteen men worked on underground. They filled two hutches, about half an hour's work, not knowing that a fall of rock barred their exit.

Rescue teams and National Fire Service personnel, seen here at the pit bottom, ran 2,000 feet of hose down the pit to fight the fire and sent an urgent message to Edinburgh for another 3,000 feet. The flames had to be extinguished before obstructions could be cleared and it was four days before the rescuers reached the bodies of the trapped men; they had been overcome by carbon monoxide gas.

It was an unusual disaster. Firedamp, or methane, was not unknown in shale workings, but it was not as common as in coal and a large build up was unprecedented. The gas, ignited by the drawer's lamp, had probably been forced out into the working area by a roof fall in the waste workings. The enquiry in Seafield Institute recommended the use of safety lamps in the Dunnet seam. Burngrange closed in 1956.

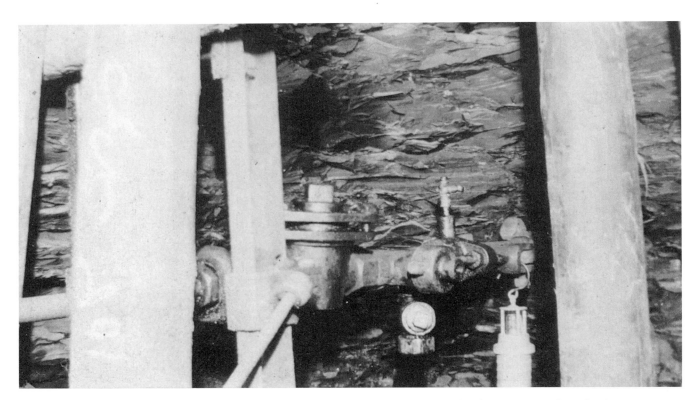

Shale was worked at Westwood, west of Livingston, for much of the industry's life. The pit was sunk to the Dunnet seam at about the 720 foot level and also worked the Broxburn seam from a cross-cut mine driven through a fault. Mine operators were required by law to test for flooding in adjacent abandoned workings and they did this with the machine in this 1920s picture, a Burnside borer. The borer drilled through a water-tight rubber seal which prevented a sudden inrush if the drill hit water.

The Government introduced a tax preference in 1928 which gave Scottish motor spirit an advantage over imported fuels. The preference was guaranteed for ten years in 1934 but only four years later this was extended and the rate increased. It gave Scottish Oils the confidence to set up a new oil-works at Westwood. It was opened in 1941. Much of the shale came from the old Westwood pit. Two benches of retorts with a distilling capacity of 1,200 tons of shale a day produced 150,000 gallons of crude oil, 30,000 gallons of naphtha and 100 tons of ammonium sulphate a week. The works closed in 1962 after the Government announced the end of the duty preference.

The legacy of the Westwood works are the dramatic five sisters bings which dominate the surrounding countryside and form a backdrop to the Freeport village outside Livingston.

The Seafield oil-works bing has been landscaped into a fake post-glacial geological feature known as a crag and tail. When this picture was taken in the early twentieth century, Seafield village contained five rows of twenty-four brick-built houses belonging to the Pumpherston Oil Company. Some of the rows were roughcast and there were pavements in front of the houses. Each house consisted of a room and kitchen with scullery, toilet, and coal cellar. Some had gardens. Drainage and water supply was good and dustbins were emptied daily. There was a wash house for every four houses, and a drying green. The contrast with other oil workers' and miners' houses was marked.

By 1919 the plethora of small oil companies that had once operated in the Lothians had been reduced to five. One of these was the great Broxburn Oil Company which operated the Broxburn oil-works and refinery and the Albyn oil-works on either side of Greendykes Road next to the Union Canal. They also retorted shale to produce crude oil, naphtha and ammonia liquor at the Roman Camp oil-works (above) to the south of the town.

In 1919 the five oil companies were taken over by Scottish Oils, a subsidiary of the Anglo-Persian Oil Company, which became British Petroleum in 1954. By that time the old Roman Camp works were in need of extensive repair, and on St Andrew's Day 1955 their gradual run-down over two years was announced. The two years were to telescope into less than one and by April 1956 they were closed.

Some oil workers were found employment at the Grangemouth and Pumpherston refineries, but displaced shale miners faced a more uncertain future. The last mines working in association with the Roman Camp works were Hopetoun Nos. 6 and 35 near Winchburgh, and this mine, Roman Camp No. 6, which worked the Camps seam. They were closed along with the oil-works.

The Broxburn Oil Company was formed in 1877 and within five years had 800 miners working in six mines to produce 800 tons of shale a day. Twenty years later the massive Broxburn works was processing 1,600 tons of shale a day; it was also using 400 tons of coal.

These men, with 'tally' (tallow) lamps on their caps, are standing beside what looks like a main and tail underground haulage system in the Hayes Craigs mine. It was one of the Broxburn Oil Company's first mines and was working in 1882. An opencast working was opened up at Hayes Craigs during the Second World War and was closed in 1960 when the associated Niddry Castle oil-works closed.

This picture gives some idea of underground conditions in a Broxburn shale mine. The hutch sitting level in the bottom right hand corner shows how steeply the seam is dipping. It appears to be close to 1 in 2, which was not unusual in shale workings. The man in the top left of the picture is using one of the hefty props as an anchor for his 'rickety', a ratchet borer which was used to drill shot holes. The shale was then blasted with gelignite and removed by hand.

Early in the twentieth century the Broxburn Oil Company owned or leased over 600 houses, and most of them were awful. There was a mix of back to back single apartments and room and kitchens, although some of these had sculleries and toilets. The other houses had to make do with outside toilets that were an affront to human dignity. When they were 'improved', each new toilet had to be shared by two families. There were insanitary open ash pits between the blocks of houses for rubbish.

Niddry Castle oil-works at Winchburgh was opened by the Oakbank Oil Company in 1903 to exploit the Duddingston shale field.

The mines associated with Niddry Castle oil-works produced 1,500 tons of shale a day, which was transported to the works by narrow-gauge electric railway (middle picture). It was one of the earliest in Scotland and ran from east of the Duntarvie Road to the Duddingston mines. The shale and materials were carried in open waggons, but there were also closed waggons for the miners. The railway continued to operate in conjunction with the oil-works, latterly linking it with two mines at Whitequarries, one at Threemiletown and the opencast site at Hayes Craigs. The closure of the oil-works was announced in 1958 and it was shut down two years later.

This pug, Hopetoun No. 1, was built by Andrew Barclay of Kilmarnock in 1908. It worked at the Hopetoun oil-works of Young's Paraffin Light and Mineral Oil Co. near Winchburgh until 1953, when it was transferred to Roman Camp where this picture was taken. It was scrapped in 1956 when the works closed.

The Pumpherston Oil Company was formed in 1883 to exploit an ammonia rich shalefield. It operated a crude oil-works and refinery at Pumpherston and took over two other crude works at Deans and Seafield which both had a number of mines feeding shale into them. The crude works at Pumpherston was closed in the 1920s, but the refinery was retained and by 1934 was the only one in the Lothians, refining crude from the other oil-works. It also refined oil from wells in Nottinghamshire and this was the only oil it was processing when it closed in 1964, bringing the Scottish shale-oil industry to an end.

Scottish Oils built a plant at Pumpherston in 1934 to make bricks from spent shale. The waste material from the bing was mixed with lime hydrate and formed by a press into bricks which were steam hardened at 480° Fahrenheit. When they emerged from the hardening process – seen here – they were grey, but weathered to a soft pink colour. The company used them to line mine workings and for buildings. They also marketed them under the brand name SOL. Despite turning out 30 million bricks a year, the works made little impact on the enormous bings.

The precise age and function of this little Pumpherston Oil Company tanker are uncertain, but it probably dates from the First World War period and is likely to have carried paraffin.

James Ross and Company built the Philpstoun oil-works beside the Union Canal in 1883. It was one of the largest crude oil-works processing 850 tons of shale a day. It was the only crude works to treat and produce its own petrol which it marketed, as seen on this advertising postcard, as Ross Petrol. The Philpstoun works closed in July 1931.

When Oakbank mine closed in 1908 the Oakbank Oil Company developed a new mine at Dedridge, Livingston. The shale was transported in buckets, on this German-designed aerial ropeway, to the oil-works adjacent to the original mine. Oakbank works closed in August 1931.

The Oakbank Oil Company village consisted of about 200 brick-built rows of primarily room and kitchen houses. Sculleries and toilets were added later, but at the time this picture was taken the tenants had to dispose of rubbish in open pits and use outside toilets. Every four households had to share a wash house and water had to be drawn from stand-pipes. Each house had a coal cellar and a few had gardens. The tenants paid a small weekly subscription for the village institute, bowling green and football pitch. The 'mountain' at the end of the street is the bing of spent shale from the oil-works. The enormous bings generated by the works have now been landscaped into low grassy or tree-topped mounds.

Early pits were often known by the name of the local farm or district, which could lead to confusion. A colliery with one name could consist of a number of shafts, each with a different name – and people compounded the problems by applying local, unofficial names. A good example is this little pit at East Calder. It was known as the Raw Pit because of its proximity to Raw Farm, yet it appears in two official lists with different names – Raw Camps and East Camps. Without the middle list there is no connection between Raw Pit and East Camps which makes research into old pits something of a minefield(!).

Raw Pit was worked by the Coltness Iron Company to win limestone, which was used as a flux in the iron smelting process. The pit was abandoned in November 1913.

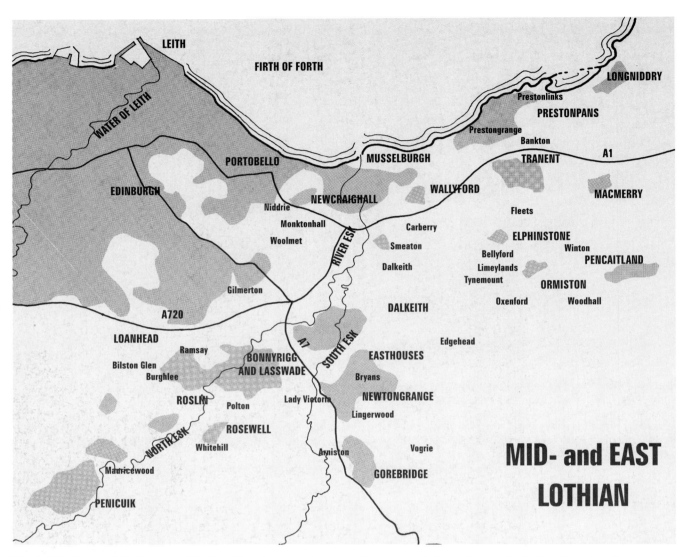

The Midlothian or Esk Basin coalfield is like a huge bath nine miles long and about four and a half miles wide. It runs roughly south-west to north-east, with Gorebridge and Penicuik at one end and Portobello and Longniddry at the other. The basin, which gets deeper as it heads out into the Firth of Forth, is made up of numerous seams which outcrop around the edge at various places. In the 1890s, a mine driven across the strata at the Ramsay pit at Loanhead intersected these twenty-two seams:

SEAM	THICKNESS	SEAM	THICKNESS
South Parrot	3 feet	Glass coal	3 feet 6 inches
Flex	5 feet	Brown's coal	2 feet 6 inches
Gas coal	3 feet	Stony coal	4 feet 6 inches
Great	8 feet	Hope's coal	2 feet
Stairhead	3 feet 4 inches	Beattie coal	3 feet
Gillespie	3 feet 4 inches	Corbie Rough	4 feet 6 inches
Blackchapel	5 feet	Corbie Splint	3 feet
Perpetual	2 feet 2 inches	Andrew's coal	4 feet
Kittlepurse	3 feet	South coal	5 feet
Peacock	5 feet	North coal	4 feet 6 inches
Rough	3 feet	North Green's	4 feet 6 inches

The Loanhead colliery was being worked by a local coal-owner in 1865 when the Shotts Iron Company, one of the giants of the Lanarkshire iron industry, took it over. They were looking for blackband ironstone, which occurs along with coal, and sunk bores to prove workable reserves. By the autumn of 1867, over 1,500 tons of ore a month were being sent back to Shotts for smelting.

Scotland's iron companies traded world-wide, but their business was disrupted in the 1860s and 70s by events like the American Civil War and the Franco-Prussian War. The Shotts Iron Company decided it would have to diversify and carried out extensive development work at Loanhead to expand its coal mining operations.

The Ramsay pit, seen here in Coal Board days, was probably named after the previous owner, R.B.W. Ramsay.

The Ramsay pit worked the 'edge coals', which are like the sides of the bath and, at Loanhead, lie on an angle of 50° to 60°. The steepness of the angle, and the unsophisticated haulage systems available in the late nineteenth century, made it very difficult to extract the coal, so the Shotts Iron Company employed an early form of 'horizon mining'. Shallow shafts were sunk alongside the rising seams and level mines were driven to intersect the coal. From this level, steep mines, or inclines, followed the seams down to a series of deeper levels, or horizons, where level cross-cut haulage roads were driven through the coal. Small teams of face men, working from these roadways, hand-hewed their way up into the coal, lowering it back down to the roads. From there it was hauled to the

inclines, raised to the pit bottom and wound to the surface. It took a special skill which men proudly handed down from father to son. Only when electric pumping and haulage was introduced in 1925 were miners able to work down into the coal for haulage back up to the roads.

The 1920s saw further development work at Ramsay. No. 2 shaft was replaced by a circular, concrete-lined shaft and a new screening plant, with picking tables and screens to grade coal according to size, was installed. A washer which also took screened coal from Roslin and Burghlee pits was erected, with an aerial ropeway to take the waste to the bing.

The Coal Board developed the pit further to produce coal from a new horizon. It put Ramsay into its 'A' category in

1962, but by the next review, three years later, it had dropped to category 'C' and closure negotiations began the following week.

The pit can be seen in the background of this picture of Loanhead Children's Day – the oldest and largest local festival in Midlothian. The day grew out of earlier play days organised by mutual benefit societies and assumed its distinctive character between 1902 and 1904 when the first School Queen was crowned. The fountain in the foreground of the picture, being used as a vantage point to watch the Queen's crowning, was gifted to the town in 1902 by Provost Hugh Kerr. It was moved in 1933 to allow for road widening, and subsequently disappeared!

200 guests were invited to the opening of the Loanhead Miners' Institute in September 1924. The ceremony was performed by Mrs Matthew Brown, wife of the Managing Director of the Shotts Iron Company. One of the main facilities was a library of 700 books provided by the local education authority.

This float from around 1917 may have been made for Loanhead's gala day parade which takes place on the Friday, eight days before the Saturday of the Children's Day. The pit-head could represent either Ramsay or Burghlee, the Shotts Iron Company's other main pit at Loanhead, to the south-west of the village. It was deeper than the Ramsay and worked the seams where they levelled out on the basin floor. Coal and men were wound in a vertical shaft and a 1,000 foot incline in the steep Great seam. A smaller incline in the Stairhead seam was used as a ventilation upcast. The skilled edge coal miners of the Ramsay pit were disdainful of the men from Lanarkshire and across the Esks who came to work the flat coals at Burghlee.

The unsophisticated pumps of the 1880s made it difficult to open up the deep seams at Burghlee. Water was pumped in stages up to the 600 foot level and drained through the Ramsay workings to a sump, from where it was pumped again up to 240 feet from the surface. From there it drained through an old tunnel known as the Mavisbank Day Level into the North Esk.

The Shotts Iron Company deepened the pit in the 1920s to work the South Parrot splint coal and planned further large-scale exploitation of the seams below the Burghlee workings. The Coal Board inherited the plans and in May 1952 Mrs William Reid, wife of the NCB's Scottish Divisional Chairman, cut the first sod of a massive new pit called Bilston Glen. Daily output was expected to reach 4,000-5,000 tons from estimated reserves of 100 million tons. Two circular shafts of 24 and 20 feet diameter were sunk, and winding levels established at 1,900 feet and 2,450 feet.

The Coal Board planted trees around the Bilston Glen site to make it look more like a modern attractive industry. Burghlee closed in 1964, shortly after the new pit was opened.

The shafts and cages at Bilston Glen had to be big enough
to take equipment like these power supports which were
used to keep mechanised faces open. They advanced with
the face, forming a kind of mobile shield above shearers
and face workers. Level roadways were driven to allow
high volume locomotive haulage. Despite all this
engineering sophistication, a 'heating incident' – the
quaint term used in the mining industry to describe a
fire – brought the pit to a standstill in August 1966.

Bilston Glen was one of the Coal Board's most successful
developments and, when test bores in the early 1970s
confirmed additional reserves, a long and profitable future
seemed assured. It became a focal point during the
national miners' strike in 1984 and, although flood water
rose to danger levels, it survived. It was one of the last
three NCB pits in Scotland, closing in 1989 along with
Barony (Ayrshire) and Monktonhall.

Lothian pits were prone to unstable roof conditions and numerous fatalities were caused by 'falls of roof' – an innocuous-sounding term that disguises the shock of a block of stone crashing to the pavement, as the floor of a pit is known. Brushers, or reddsmen, had the dangerous job of clearing loose rock from roofs or walls of roadways before it fell.

In longwall mining, the method used on the fully mechanised faces at Bilston Glen, the face was advanced between parallel roads about two hundred yards apart. The sides of the road were built up with solid walls of rock, known as packs. Between the roads and behind the faceline the roof was left to collapse. As the face advanced, the roof could remain unsupported for a long time. When it 'hung' for a long time, even miners who knew what to expect got nervous waiting for it to crack. The sandstone roof in this dramatic picture of the Great seam workings at Bilston Glen has hung too long and given way in front of the face line.

Opposite: The Shotts Iron Company took a lease on the Roslin field in 1898 and three years later started to sink a new shaft. When they hit a bed of shifting sand the engineers and sinkers quickly realised they had met their match and started another shaft, twenty-five feet away. By June 1903 they had reached a high-quality household coal at 480 feet. The shaft was refitted in 1922 and doubled in depth. At the same time a 1,200 foot dook, or underground mine, was driven to the Peacock seam. The screening plant was extended in the 1920s and pit-head baths, believed to have been the first in the Lothians, were opened in 1930.

These two pictures are taken from the 1920s photograph album of a mining student whose idea of a summer vacation was a tour Scotland's collieries. He describes these Roslin workings as steep, varying between 30° and 75°. Roslin worked both the steep edge seams and the flat seams on the basin floor.

A brickworks was set up at Roslin in 1937 and the following year was producing 40,000 bricks a day. Bricks were needed early in the war to make air-raid shelters, but by 1943 demand had dried up and 1.5 million bricks remained unsold. The works was put on a care and maintenance basis and taken over along with the pit by the NCB. Roslin was threatened with closure in 1962, but was reprieved after output improved. It was closed in 1969. This picture shows No. 1 headframe viewed from No. 2, with the village in the background. The pit's nickname was the Moat.

The New St. Matthew's Church, Rosewell.
Near the old St. Matthew's, Roslin, Midlothian.

Three miners walk down Carnethie Street, Rosewell, while a bowler-hatted gent keeps his distance on the footpath. The village was between two collieries, Whitehill and Polton, which were both operated by the Lothian Coal Company after it was formed in 1890.

Whitehill (or Rosewell as it was also called) originally had two shafts for ventilation and pumping, and two 10 foot diameter winding shafts close together. Latterly they were used only for man winding, and a haulage mine was used to bring coal to the surface. Whitehill is thought to have been the first pit in Scotland to use coal cutters. The machines, driven by compressed air, were made in the colliery workshops in the 1870s; two worked in the Jewel coal and a third in the Splint. Although Polton was closed prior to nationalisation, Whitehill was taken into Coal Board ownership and had its underground haulage system developed into one of the most modern in Scotland. It was closed in 1961.

Some local buildings, most notably St Matthew's Church in Rosewell, were built with bricks from the Whitehill brickworks, and remain as a tangible reminder of this once busy colliery.

Whitehill was used as the location for the film 'The Brave Don't Cry', about the disaster and dramatic rescue at Knockshinnoch Castle colliery in Ayrshire in 1950.

THE MAURICEWOOD DISASTER

The worst mining disaster in the Lothians took place at the Shotts Iron Company's Mauricewood pit to the north of Penicuik. The pit had been sunk in the 1870s to work ironstone, but when that became unprofitable it was developed to work coal as well. The seams dipped at an angle of 50° and the pit was developed along similar lines to the Ramsay at Loanhead to reach the deeper measures. A single shaft was sunk to 500 feet and from its base, steep parallel inclined mines were driven for 960 feet. They were intersected by horizontal roads at 240 foot intervals. One of the inclines was used for winding and ventilation downcast, while the other, containing steam pipes and an escape ladder, was used as the upcast. The second means of egress, required by law, was a 1,000 yard communications road to the adjacent Greenlaw mine.

Seventy men and boys were underground on 5th September 1889 when a fire broke out in an engine house at the deepest level. Some boys were seen running into the workings to raise the alarm by a man who had just started being hauled up the incline. It was the last time they were seen alive. Halfway up his ascent the man on the haulage bogie encountered smoke pouring through an open ventilation door; it should have been shut. Smoke and poisonous fumes were being blown back into the pit and every man's life was in danger.

Initially the fumes prevented rescuers from getting past the door. Once it was closed and sealed they reached the lower level where they found about twenty bodies and a raging fire. Attempts to extinguish it had to be abandoned and the pit was sealed and flooded. It was inspected six weeks later, but the fire was still burning and the pit had to be sealed again. It was not reopened until the following March. The remaining bodies were recovered from behind a wall of stones and clay which the men had built to hold back the fumes. They had not died quickly.

A disaster fund was set up and continued to provide funds to the bereaved relatives up to the 1920s. The pit worked intermittently after the disaster and was abandoned in 1909. It has assured Penicuik an unwelcome place in the mining heritage of the Lothians.

The company village of Shottstown, seen here in the 1890s, was built to house the Mauricewood miners and their families. It was demolished in the late 1950s and the bing removed shortly after when it started to smoulder. The Miners' Welfare and Social Club perpetuates the Shottstown name.

Every pit, or group of pits employing over a hundred men, was required by the Coal Mines Act of 1911 to have a trained rescue brigade. The Act also required coal-owners to set up permanently manned rescue stations for their areas. Collieries in West Lothian came under the Lanarkshire Coalmasters Association who set up a rescue station in Coatbridge in 1915. The Lothian coalmasters took just as long to get their rescue station operational. It was in the old Castle Brewery in the Grassmarket in Edinburgh which was purchased in 1913 by the George Heriot Trust. It was converted and attached to the Heriot-Watt School of Mining and opened by the Lord Provost of Edinburgh in February 1915.

Training was made as realistic as possible. Fumes could be injected into the long smoke gallery which was set up round three sides of the old brewery cellars. The old brewery well was used to simulate a shaft. Would-be brigadesmen had to clear debris and attend to 'casualties' in realistic situations, or carry a 140 pound dummy on a stretcher over rubble-strewn heated passages that simulated underground conditions. The training was tough and only the fittest and ablest became brigadesmen.

George Kirkwood, the tall brigadesman third from the right in this picture of the Newbattle and Lingerwood brigade of 1926, was an Ayrshire man who worked for a few years in Fife and the Lothians after graduating from the Royal College of Technology in Glasgow. He went back to his native county but returned to the Lothians as the NCB's first Area General Manager when the industry was nationalised.

When the Heriot-Watt mining school closed in 1968 the Mines Rescue Station was moved to Lingerwood colliery. As the industry contracted further the rescue service in Scotland was concentrated at Crossgates in Fife.

After the Reformation of 1560 and the dissolution of the monasteries, the Newbattle coal workings along the South Esk were taken over by the Lothian family. When the Marquis of Lothian granted a lease to the newly formed Lothian Coal Company in 1890, coal was being worked from three pits – Bryans, Dickson's, and the Engine pit – a name widely used to describe an old shaft worked by a steam winding engine. This engine pit was sunk in 1798 and worked the steep edge coals along with Dickson's pit. Both had reached the limit of their haulage depth at over 800 feet when work started on the sinking of a major new shaft 500 yards to the west. It was known as the Lady Victoria, after the wife of the Marquis of Lothian. The old Engine pit became known as Lingerwood and can be seen here in the 1960s with the 'Lady Vic' behind.

Sinking of the Lady Victoria began in August 1890. It was the first shaft in Scotland to be sunk and walled simultaneously, but making it watertight retarded progress. Water feeding at a rate of 100 gallons a minute was encountered at 600 feet and, 180 feet lower, another feeder of 200 gallons a minute was cut. The shaft was taken down to 1,740 feet, but had to be back-filled to a working depth of 1,624 feet when more water was encountered. Even so it was the deepest in Scotland at the time. The shaft was connected underground to the old Lingerwood workings, giving them a new lease of life. The new pit opened in 1895.

Although indistinct and shaky, this is a rare picture of the old Bryans pit which worked the outcropping seams between Newtongrange and Easthouses.

This great winding engine was made by Grant, Ritchie of Kilmarnock, one of the foremost makers of colliery equipment in Scotland. The 20 foot diameter winding drum was 10 feet 6 inches wide. It was powered by steam and driven by two horizontal cylinders with a 7 foot stroke. The engine house originally had a pitch-pine floor, oak-lined walls and teak cladding round the cylinders, but this woodwork was extensively damaged by a fire in 1903. The engine was rebuilt with a new right-hand cylinder and was still working when the pit closed in 1981.

There were two landing stages at the top and bottom of the shaft and the double-decked cages could raise twelve loaded hutches or forty-eight men in a single lift. Later the size of the hutches was increased and the number wound in each cage reduced to eight. On the surface, the hutches from the lower deck, on the left, were raised by creeper chain to join those from the upper deck and all were moved by gravity to the weighing machines and tipplers (rotating cradles which held the hutches while tipping the coal from them). The shaft is seen rising through the centre right of the picture.

The underground main roads at the pit were made to dimensions that, at the time, were regarded as over generous. They were 8 feet high, arched at the top, and 10 or 12 feet wide. The dimensions were even more generous at the pit bottom. The critics were proved wrong because the roads were able to take larger hutches and move substantially more coal to the pit bottom than smaller roads would have done. The main roads were worked by a surface mounted haulage system; 120 ponies were originally used for haulage to the main roads.

When this picture of the deep Jewel seam workings was taken in 1924, five other seams were also being worked. The 7 foot thick Great seam was the most productive, the others were the Splint, Kailblades, Coronation and Diamond seams. The Newbattle collieries operated a system of roof support which used timber props inside a weldless steel tube. The steel props were pre-cut to size for each seam and used in conjunction with 6 foot long corrugated steel straps which helped to support a larger area of roof. They also gave face men a measure of protection from shaly roof material that was prone to collapse. The steel props were recovered as the face advanced.

This impressive battery of twelve boilers was installed just after the First World War. They were made in Manchester and purchased as war surplus stock. They provided power not just for steam winding and haulage, but also for the final lift of a staged pumping system that forced 800 gallons a minute 900 feet to the surface. Lady Victoria was always a wet pit and something like 5,000 tons of water, the equivalent of two and a half times the weight of coal raised, was pumped out daily.

The Newbattle collieries operated their own engineering workshops which were moved from an original site at Lingerwood to a new building at Lady Victoria. The workshops made a lot of the colliery equipment, repaired their own waggons and locomotives, and designed a lot of the innovative features incorporated in the underground workings. These workshops established a tradition that the National Coal Board built on when they based the Lothian Area's central workshops at Lady Victoria.

Baths for the Lady Victoria and Lingerwood collieries were opened in June 1954. Their installation had been resisted for a long time and the credit for the change of heart goes to local women who were no doubt fed up with men coming home in filthy clothes. There were baths and lockers for over 3,000 men, a canteen, medical centre and bottle filling facilities. A heated walkway, seen on the left here, linked the baths to Lady Victoria on the other side of the A7 road. Provision was also made for car, bus and bicycle parking.

The Lady Vic was regarded by the Coal Board as a major unit and was used on the east side of the Esk Basin to match Bilston Glen on the west. Output rose by about 40% in the first five years of public ownership and despite a closure scare in the 1960s it continued working until 1981. The colliery is now the location of the Scottish Mining Museum.

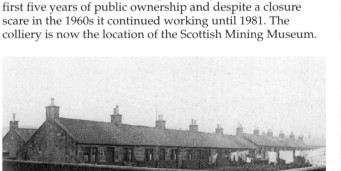

Newtongrange very quickly became the largest village of Newbattle Parish. It was begun by the Marquis of Lothian and expanded by the Lothian Coal Company for miners working at their collieries. It had running water and decent sanitation, but as ever with tied housing, tenants had to work for the company and do its bidding, however unreasonable, or face eviction. Newtongrange is now a conservation village.

Easthouses mine was opened by the Lothian Coal Company in 1909. It was driven at an incline of 1 in 2 in the outcropping coal. The NCB mechanised it and were proud of its record as one of the few operations in Europe where 100% of the output was won by power loading. The Great seam was worked by slow-speed ploughs which shaved 12 inch slices of coal from four longwall faces. The coal was brought up the steep gradient by a surface-mounted steam haulage engine that could raise 1,000 tons a shift in 9 ton mine cars. The upper picture, of the engine house, was taken at the end of the 1960s after worsening roof conditions had forced the mine's closure. The lower picture shows the engine, which was installed in the 1950s.

The treatment plant for the three Newbattle units was at Lady Victoria and coal was brought to it from Lingerwood and Easthouses by the collieries' own railway system. Local youngsters used to hitch rides on the coal waggons coming from Easthouses and made nuisances of themselves by pelting passers-by with lumps of coal.

Easthouses village, seen here in the 1890s with children dressed up for a special day, perhaps a Sunday School outing, was transformed in the 1950s by the expanding coal industry. A 'new town' was built for incoming mining families, but when Easthouses mine closed Midlothian County Council saw their worst fears of single industry towns realised. Some men found work in Lady Victoria, Bilston Glen and Monktonhall, but there were redundancies.

Shallow pits which were drained through dipping mines into the Gore Burn had worked the edge coals for many years in the Arniston/Gorebridge area before the Arniston Colliery's Emily pit was sunk. It worked at the 600 foot level. In the 1860s a new shaft was sunk to 960 feet making it the deepest pit in the east of Scotland. It opened up the Splint coal at 750 feet and the valuable Parrot coal 210 feet lower. The new shaft could raise 30 tons of coal and pump the equivalent of 174 tons of water an hour.

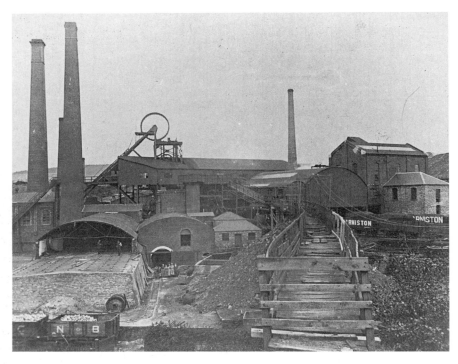

The deep shaft also worked as a ventilation downcast. Shortly before it was sunk, legislation was introduced requiring pits to have more than one means of access and egress, for safety and ventilation. Arniston already met this requirement, but the value of an additional means of escape was proved in August 1937 when 140 men were caught underground by the collapse of the upcast ventilation shaft. They were brought up without panic, but with the colliery out of action for at least three weeks, nearly 1,200 men were out of work. The Ministry of Labour opened a temporary office in Newbyres Hall in Gorebridge to deal with men's unemployment claims. The old headgear, which had collapsed, was found years later at the bottom of the shaft.

The upper picture shows the Emily pit early in the twentieth century, with a hutch road that once led to the waste bing in the foreground and the ovens where bricks were fired on the left. The lower picture shows the pit in 1962.

The Arniston Coal Company was set up in 1874 and immediately started sinking the Gore pit. It was completed in 1878. The rectangular shaft was 700 feet deep and, like the deep Emily shaft, the top 120 feet was lined (Emily's with stone, Gore's with brick) with timber lining below. Each cage could raise four, nine hundredweight hutches in one wind. Underground mines were driven from the base of the shaft to the Parrot, Great and Splint seams.

The Gore pit was sunk alongside the famous 'Waverley' rail route from Edinburgh to Hawick and Carlisle. The upper picture shows it in British Railways' days with a former LNER V2 class locomotive speeding past. The lower picture was taken just before the colliery closed in 1962.

When the NCB announced its first serious round of closures in 1959 Arniston was spared, although some underground areas were closed. Full closure was announced in 1961. Arniston became a depot for colliery spares where second-hand machinery, stored in a tent-like dome, could be selected for use at other pits.

This picture of the electricity generating station at the Emily pit shows that not every bit of a colliery was covered in coal dust and stoor. The men who looked after such places were very house-proud and insisted on people having clean feet before they trod on the highly polished floor. It was not until the NCB days that all pits took their power from the national grid.

Money was deducted from miners' wages to pay for the services of blacksmiths, like these at Arniston. They were essential to the working of any pit, and made and maintained pit equipment, fitted shoes to the ponies and kept the miners' pick heads sharp. In the days before universal education, some highly intelligent men worked in pits and they put their ingenuity to good use, improvising tools and equipment.

In the early hours of a November morning in 1909 the explosives magazine by the Emily pit-bing blew up. Sabotage by a disgruntled employee was suspected, but the cause was not established. The magazine was a well built brick structure surrounded by an earth bank and a high fence of railway sleepers. All that was left was a hole in the ground. Debris was hurled in all directions, windows in nearby buildings were broken, roof tiles were smashed and the doors of the Gorebridge Co-op burst in. The blast was followed by the sound of the colliery hooter. Miners rushed out of their homes prepared to assist in a rescue, but found rubble-strewn streets instead.

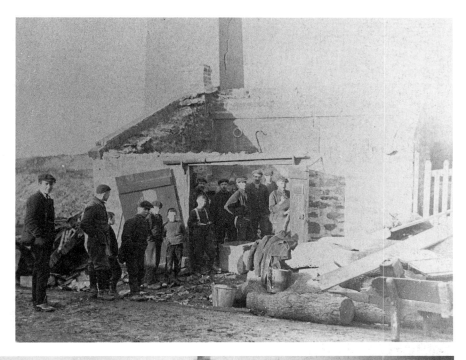

It may have been a tight squeeze for all six men to cram into, but Arniston's rescue team were very proud of their little van, seen here in the mid-1950s. Behind it is the rescue room which every pit had to have. It was used as a base if there was an incident and for first aid training. The brigadesmen kept clothing and equipment in it too. Arniston rescue teams had a proud tradition and were frequent competition winners. Their great rivals in inter-brigade competitions were Prestongrange colliery and when three members of each team formed the Monktonhall team, they won the area cup an unprecedented five years running.

One of the most popular of recreations in mining communities was band music. This Arniston colliery band was known as the Clean Cut Silver Band, a reference perhaps to a conductor's liking for a 'clean cut', with all of the players stopping abruptly, together.

Pipe band music was also popular with miners. The Arniston Colliery Pipe Band was formed in the early 1920s, but had no proper uniform until 1924 when this picture was probably taken.

In 1905 William Hennessey, the eldest son of a mining family from near Gorebridge, heard a dog barking continuously. He traced the sound to an old 80 foot deep air shaft and set about trying to rescue the distressed animal. He put a piece of meat into his mother's clothes basket and lowered it with a rope. Time and again the dog got into the basket only to fall out again as William started to raise it. Resisting suggestions of pouring stones down the shaft to put the animal out of its misery he kept going until the dog was rescued. It had a stone tied round its neck – somebody had thrown it down the shaft to kill it! William kept 'Glen' and later put his interest in animals to good use when he left the pits to become a gamekeeper.

A miner turning gamekeeper was much the same as a poacher doing so. Many miners kept lurchers like this one, and loved nothing better than to roam the countryside in search of hares and other game. Quite what part the pipes played in such activities is hard to guess at. This group of Gorebridge men may, of course, be entirely innocent of any underhand activity. On the other hand . . . !

The Jack pit at Vogrie was operated by the Arniston Coal Company and, around 1900, was winning a variety of coals and fireclay. By the 1920s Vogrie coal was being sold in border towns like Selkirk. The pit was being worked by Gavin Paul and Sons, but they extended the roads too far and it became unworkable and closed.

The old coal and fireclay industries provided work for many people, like this group at the Vogrie brickworks. Women, and men who had been hurt and were no longer fit to work underground, were often given jobs as surface workers.

This little colliery is believed to be
Edgehead, to the east of
Newtongrange. It was opened about
1850 and operated by the Earl of Stair
with only ten men underground and
two on the surface. It was taken over
from the Stair Estates by the Fordell
Mains (Midlothian) Colliery Co.
around 1930, but appears to have been
moribund by 1947. The NCB worked a
mine at Edgehead until 1959.

This limestone working, with daylight
flooding in, is an undercut extension
of the Esperston quarries to the south
of Gorebridge. The stone has been
worked by stoop and room mining
techniques. The miners, or in this case
quarrymen, have cut into the mineral
being worked to form spaces, known
as rooms, around columns of stone
known as stoops. The workings were
taken to the limit of intended
operations and then the men worked
back removing the columns and
allowing the roof to collapse behind
them. Here the somewhat slender
stone columns are getting extra
support from some equally slender
wooden props.

If the Midlothian coalfield is like a bath, the East Lothian field is a wash-hand basin of about 30 square miles on the east side of the Roman Camp ridge. Neither coalfield observes the man-made county boundaries; Carberry and Wallyford pits operated in the East Lothian field while the Prestonpans pits worked the Midlothian.

Fleets colliery, to the south of Tranent, was almost at the centre of the East Lothian field. No. 1 pit was sunk in the 1850s or 60s to the Great seam and re-sunk to the Splint in the 1880s. It was always a very wet pit and this Cornish beam pumping engine, made in 1847 at the Perran Foundry, is believed to have been installed at the time of the re-sinking. It was transferred from Dolphinston No. 1 pit which was abandoned around 1885.

Elphinstone village was associated with Fleets and Howden pits which were known as the Elphinstone collieries. The pits were worked by succeeding generations of the Durie family and the family company of R. and J. Durie Ltd. before they were taken over by the Edinburgh Collieries Company. The main shafts were on either side of an east-west fault and ventilated by forcing fans. The upcast for Fleets was nearly a mile to the west and the Catherine shaft, a quarter of a mile from Howden, worked as its upcast.

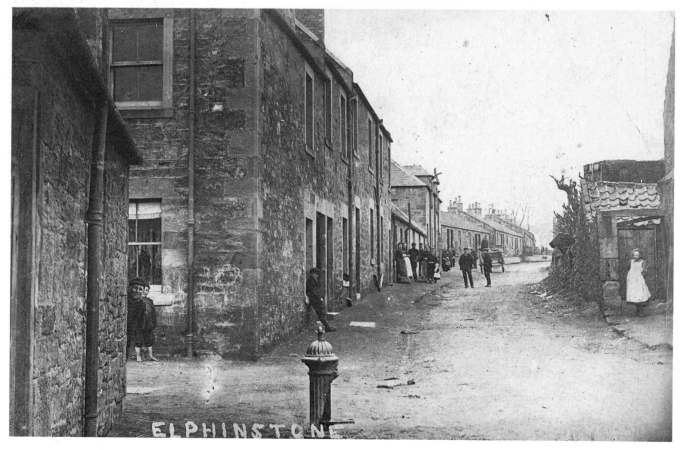

ELPHINSTONE

Fleets was the first winner of the Wilson Shield, a Second World War output competition in which each competing colliery was set a target figure to beat. Fleets exceeded its monthly target with a four week average output of 120.6%. Burghlee was second with an output of 117.2% and Whitehill third with a figure of 115.2%. Fleets closed early in 1959.

Four drift mines, Winton, Bellyford, Oxenford No. 3 and Castle formed the NCB's Ormiston scheme. It was designed to replace obsolete operations at Oxenford No. 2 (Airfield), Tynemount and Limeylands pits. Winton had been opened as a ventilation mine in 1943 by the Ormiston Coal Company, but the Board redeveloped it in 1949/50 to work coal (above and left). It closed in 1962.

The Woodhall Coal Company had only one pit, the Pencaitland or Tyneholm colliery, about a mile from Wester Pencaitland. Sinking began in 1903. The pit was expected to be in production for no more than twenty years, but favourable geological conditions allowed it to continue until 1944. It worked the south-eastern corner of the East Lothian field and cleaned out the rising seams to where they outcropped; to the extent that men could come up through holes to the surface for a smoke. To begin with the company had more orders for its coal than miners to dig it. To make it easier for men to get to the pit, a passenger platform was built beside the colliery on the Gifford and Garvald Railway. It does not appear to have attracted many men because miners' specials were discontinued after only a few months.

These men are sitting at the entrance to a small private drift mine called Penkaet. It was opened in the 1930s. This kind of opening was known by Scottish miners as an in-gaun-e'e (in going eye).

Around 1900, the Penston collieries of Deans and Moore worked the 2 foot 4 inch thick Kailblades seam at a depth of 775 feet. The field was free of faults and remarkably level with only slight undulating dips. Headroom in the roads was only 4 feet above the hutch rails. The roads were run from a number of shafts, all apparently with winding gear: the Merryfield pit was 500 yards from the Engine pit, which also had pumping engines, and 800 yards to the west of Merryfield was another shaft. There was another at Greendykes and the North pit was 600 yards from it in the direction of Saint Germains.

The pit in this picture was known as Penston No. 1, Mont Fair or Macmerry. It was sunk about 1894, taken over by the Udston Coal Company about 1906 and closed by 1914.

Macmerry was a mining and iron-working community and these rows are similar to those found elsewhere in Scotland where coal and iron were worked together. The local Gladsmuir Ironworks gave the village its nickname, the Blast.

Scotland's earliest
railway was a wooden
railed waggonway laid in
1722 to connect collieries
at Tranent to the harbour
at Cockenzie. In 1745 Sir
John Cope deployed his
troops along it in an
attempt to stop Bonnie
Prince Charlie from
marching on England,
but, at the Battle of
Prestonpans, the
Jacobites cut them to
pieces. The waggonway
went back to carrying
coals and was fitted with
iron rails in 1815. By the
1870s only the end of the
line near Tranent was in
use and full gauge track
was laid astride the old
rails (although they
continued to be used
until about 1886).

The main Edinburgh to Berwick railway line crossed the old waggonway at Meadowmill. A washery was set up there to treat coal from Bankton colliery which was sunk about 1901 in association with Prestonlinks colliery. It later treated coal from other collieries, but was closed when the Dalkeith Central Preparation Plant was opened. The NCB put down a drift mine at Meadowmill in 1951; it closed in 1960. The site was used as a coal depot for some time after and as a distribution point for miners' concessionary coal. The old washery bings and pit-head baths are seen here behind the railway trucks.

Messrs Nimmo and Co. of Slammanan leased the minerals on the Bankton and Prestonlinks estates in 1899 and formed a company called Forth Collieries Ltd. to explore the reserves beyond a whinstone barrier a mile out from the shore. Prestonlinks colliery was developed on the site of a pit, abandoned since 1884, on the foreshore at Cockenzie. The No. 2 shaft was reopened and a new No. 3 pit sunk. The roadway drivage into the whinstone dyke began in April 1903, with mine drivers using compressed air drills and blasting with gelignite. They advanced at a rate of 21 feet a week and after 110 feet of rock hit a seven foot seam, proving that coal stretched from the Lothians to Fife. Edinburgh Collieries took the pit over, sunk a new No. 4 ventilation pit in 1912 and filled in the old No. 1 shaft. They still operated the pit at the time of nationalisation.

This Prestonlinks brigade won the first rescue competition for Mid- and East Lothian in 1922 and was presented with a silver challenge cup awarded by the Lothians Welfare Committee.

The Coal Board initially predicted a long life for Prestonlinks, but they put it into their 'C' category in 1962 and closed it in 1964. This gave rise to a widely held view amongst former miners that it was sacrificed to make way for Cockenzie power station which was built on the site soon after. Many of the men were bussed daily to Monktonhall which provided the coal for Cockenzie.

Wiles' Buses of Port Seton provided the service. They had operated Coal Board contracts from the time of nationalisation up to when Prestonlinks became the last colliery in East Lothian to close. They won the contract to ferry miners to Monktonhall and continued to honour it even through some difficult times during the 1984 strike. They were still transporting miners up to 1989 when the combination of Monktonhall's mothballing and the deregulation of bus operations caused the company to cease trading.

Coal, outcropping close to the sea, was used by monks to fire salt pans on the shore at Prestonpans. Prestongrange colliery developed later as a number of shallow, self-draining mines and the area remained a salt-making centre until the abrogation of salt duty in 1825. At about the same time a Newcastle mining engineer, Matthias Dunn, took out a lease at Prestongrange and sunk two shafts, 28 yards apart, to work deeper coals. One 10 foot square shaft was for winding and the other, 10 feet by 5, was used for pumping. Dunn gave the pit up around 1838.

Prestongrange colliery was developed next to the small harbour of Morison's Haven which was built for the Abbot of Newbattle to trade salt and coal for French wine and other commodities in the sixteenth century. It was later used to export fireclay products as well as coal. There were two berths for the fireclay works and four coaling berths, all connected by railways or tramways to the colliery and kilns. Vessels of up to 280 tons could enter the harbour and around 1900, almost one a day was leaving with exports.

The pit appears to have been worked intermittently by the Grant-Suttie family after 1838. It was reopened in 1874 by the Prestongrange Coal and Iron Company. The No. 2 shaft was redeveloped to work the Jewel coal and No. 1 shaft used to pump the huge quantities of water in the pit. A beam pumping-engine made by Harvey and Company of Hayle in Cornwall was installed. It was shipped to Morison's Haven and erected in a massive stone pump-house beside the 'water' shaft. The front wall of the house was six feet thick to support the weight and motion of the thirty-three foot cast iron beam.

Inside the house was an enormous cylinder, driven by high pressure steam. It pulled the inner end of the beam down, raising the outer end to which was attached a 100 ton Oregon pine pump rod. When the beam had risen to its full height, the rod dropped under its own weight. At the end of its stroke it was pulled back up by the cylinder and the rise and fall action was repeated at an average of three and a half strokes per minute. The speed could be adjusted depending on the amount of water to be raised. In 1905 the engine was modified to work three pumps and the beam strengthened to take the additional load. The engine remained in service until 1954. It has been preserved as the central attraction of the Prestongrange Industrial Heritage Museum.

The colliery remained under the ownership of the Grant-Sutties of Prestongrange House until 1895 when the Summerlee and Mossend Iron and Steel Company took it over. At the time only two seams were being worked, the eight foot thick Great seam, and the four foot Jewel seam. The Summerlee Co. re-equipped the pit. They sunk a No. 3 ventilation shaft and opened out the deeper Beggar seam, increasing output to 500 tons a day. Prestongrange also produced a good quality fireclay which went to make firebricks, tiles and pipes. In the early twentieth century the brickworks was making 3 million refractory firebricks a year while a separate works produced tiles and pipes. Between them they manufactured 5,500 tons of clay products a year.

The beehive-shaped kilns, behind the wall in the foreground, were rebuilt by the Coal Board who also carried out other redevelopment work at the pit. New pit-head baths, the 100th in Scotland, were opened in September 1952 by sixty-six year old William Cunningham, a miner who had spent nearly all of his fifty-two working years at the colliery. East Lothian County Council Roads Committee saved the Coal Board the cost of a new access gantry by diverting the Musselburgh to Prestonpans coast road around them. The pit closed in 1962.

The Summerlee and Mossend Iron and Steel Co. became the Summerlee Iron Company in 1898. They operated a wonderfully varied looking fleet of elderly pugs at Prestongrange. The upper picture from the 1940s, shows a locomotive built by Falcon Engineering of Loughborough in 1884. It is working on the bing which eventually filled in and covered the old Morison's Haven harbour. The man with a sack has been scavenging for coal. The middle picture is of an Andrew Barclay pug of 1881 and the lower picture is of another Barclay pug of 1869.

Working pugs form an important element of the Prestongrange Industrial Heritage Museum which was set up by former colliery manager, David Spence, when the pit closed.

The Summerlee Iron Company moved many mining families from Lanarkshire to Prestonpans to work their newly acquired pit. They built this street of brick upstairs-downstairs housing and named it, immodestly, Summerlee Street.

SUMMERLEE STREET, PRESTONPANS.

The contrast between the miners' housing and Prestongrange House, the home of the former coal-owner Sir George Grant-Suttie Bt, could hardly be greater. The last of the Grant-Suttie family to live there, Lady Susan, gave it up during the First World War and it was used to house conscientious objectors. After the war the grounds were turned into a golf course for the Royal Musselburgh Golf Club. They struggled to maintain the course and house and in 1958 Prestongrange was bought by the Coal Industry Social Welfare Organisation – a rare instance of miners taking over the estate of their former employer. CISWO continues to support the golf club and the Scottish Coalfield Championships are played on the course every year. The clubhouse is somewhat grander than the old East and West Prestonpans Institutes.

The Royal Musselburgh Golf Club (INSTITUTED 1774)

West Welfare Institute, Prestonpans.

East Welfare Institute, Prestonpans.

The Engine and Bye pits at Wallyford were sunk to the Great seam in 1857 and a No. 3 shaft sunk later. Nos. 2 and 3 were deepened to the Parrot Rough and, after coal-owners Deans and Moore took over in 1891, re-sunk to the Jewel. They worked a field of nearly 20,000 acres, half of which was under the sea. In 1900 the pit was taken over by Edinburgh Collieries who confidently expected output levels to be sustained for 200 years. It was one of the industry's wilder estimates – the pit had closed before the Coal Board took over. The miners' row on the right has been replaced by newer housing in what is now Salters Road.

Miners' institutes, like this one at Wallyford, were set up following the Mining Industries Act of 1920. A penny was levied on every ton of coal produced to establish a fund which was used to provide welfare facilities for mining communities. Four fifths of the money had to be spent in the area where it was raised. The fund was administered by a central Miners' Welfare Committee and local committees determined what kind of facilities were wanted. A feature of institutes in the Lothian area was the provision of libraries as well as the usual social hall, meeting rooms and games facilities. Institutes in West Lothian came under the Lanarkshire area committee.

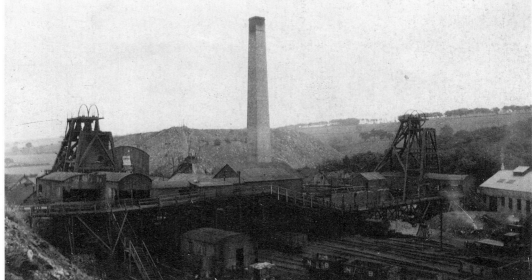

These three pictures appear to be of Carberry colliery. It was just over a mile south-east of the old Inveresk Station, and like Wallyford was operated by Deans and Moore before being taken over by Edinburgh Collieries when the company was formed in 1900. Some of their waggons, bearing the full Edinburgh Collieries Company Limited title, can be seen in the foreground of the upper picture. Carberry and Wallyford worked the south-western corner of the East Lothian basin and the coal bore a strong resemblance to that won at Woodhall.

Carberry Nos. 1 and 2 were sunk to 450 feet in 1866 to work the Great seam; the Jewel was reached later. No. 1 shaft appears to have been disused when No. 3 shaft was sunk about 1900 to work the Diamond, Kailblades and Hauchielin coals. The coalfield lay on an angle of about 1 in 3 and was traversed by two large faults, a mile apart. Between them the field was free of disturbance, but each fault dropped, or 'threw', the coal measures by 150 feet, taking the workings down to 750 feet. An early Coal Board estimate suggested that the colliery could have another 100 years' life, but a dozen years later, in April 1960, it was closed.

In the days before mechanical man-riders, miners moved quickly on foot along low roads in a stooped position, like a 'half-shut knife'. Simply getting to the working place at the coal face was physically demanding and once there, men worked up even more of a sweat shovelling coal or shoving hutches. The coal dust stuck to their sweaty skin – the more greasy a man's skin the blacker he got, like this boy from Carberry. The heavy work and dusty atmosphere meant that miners constantly needed to keep their mouths moist and, tucked under the young man's arm is that essential item of miner's kit, a battered tin flask. It would be filled with water or, if his mother was looking after him well, with cold sweet tea.

Men needed more than water or tea to sustain them during an underground shift and as well as a flask they carried sandwiches in a 'piece' tin. These two unidentified men, with their tally lamps slung from their pockets, have casually dropped their tins at their feet. Shaped with a rounded end to fit a slice of plain bread, the tins held three pieces. They were unlikely to win the culinary acclaim given to the pasties of Cornish tin-miners. Cheese, on its own or with jam or lemon curd, was a standard filling, but some men stuffed chocolate bars between slices of bread. Others put a slice of toast with their pieces to keep them fresh. Pieces that had been underground were said to have a distinctive flavour and children used to chivvy miners for any they brought back up to the surface.

This group of young miners is thought to have been photographed at Dalkeith around 1905. They are wearing the typical pit clothes of the time and, hooked onto their soft cloth caps are tallow or tally lamps. They had a wick which led down the funnel of the lamp to a reservoir filled with seal oil or wax. Miners softened wax in their hands before stuffing it into their lamps and the heat from the burning wick softened it further.

A. and G. Moore & Co. drove roads into rising ground near Dalkeith around 1907 to intersect with seams inclined at about 1 in 2. These new mines were in a somewhat isolated location and the company had to bring men from Musselburgh and the surrounding area to work them. To solve the constant transport problems they engaged the architects Messrs Hamilton of Edinburgh and Tranent to design a new village. It was known as Smeaton. The first seventy-two houses were started in 1907 and work to build another seventy-two began soon after.

Eventually four mines were opened at Smeaton. They extracted coal lying below the seams being worked from five similar drift mines at Dalkeith. The NCB closed the Smeaton mines almost immediately and concentrated development at Dalkeith. Nos. 5 and 9 mines were used for drawing coal, No. 6 for ventilation and Nos. 7 and 8 for access. A further man-haulage mine, No. 10, was started, but had to be abandoned when it hit wet running sand. Dalkeith was a successful and profitable operation that worked by conventional methods where the coal was undercut by machine, blasted and removed by hand. Unstable roof conditions were not conducive to full mechanisation and attempts to introduce shearers hastened the mines' demise. They closed in 1978. The upper picture shows an early haulage engine at Smeaton, the lower picture shows the later underground workings at Dalkeith.

The story of mining in the Dalkeith area might have been different if the Board had gone ahead with plans announced at the height of its honeymoon period. In 1954 test bores apparently proved six seams of good coal adjacent to No. 9 mine. The sinking of a new pit, with two shafts to be known as Dalkeith 11 and 12, was planned to work an area of over 580 acres and produce 1,000 tons a day for 60 years. Midlothian County Council were wary and imposed tight planning conditions which were not to the Board's liking. Eighteen months later they abandoned the plans blaming faulting in the seams.

The Board upgraded their original plans for a washer at Dalkeith No. 9 mine and built Scotland's first central preparation plant instead. It was opened in 1953. The output of all the nearby collieries was sent to it and its initial capacity of 1,500 tons a day was expected to rise to 3,000 tons. It effected considerable economies, replacing four old washeries and ten picking tables. One of those washeries was at Smeaton, but although it was shut, the bing continued to be used by the Dalkeith preparation plant with the waste being taken to Smeaton by aerial ropeway. This won few friends at Smeaton. Not only were their mines and washery closed, but somebody else's rubbish was being dumped on their doorstep, on a burning, smelly and polluting bing.

The sidings at Dalkeith did away with the need for shunting locomotives or inclines. This traverser moved loaded waggons, at the push of a button, from the washer to an appropriate siding.

Railways made big mining developments possible away from the coasts and the resultant rise in exports had a big impact on Leith. The first rail link into the port was a horse-drawn branch line from the Edinburgh and Dalkeith Railway in 1838. Locomotive haulage was introduced by the North British Railway when they took it over, and other lines were laid into the docks through the nineteenth century. Millions of tons of coal were exported annually through the port and large quantities of pit props came in.

The two pictures present an interesting contrast in technology. In the upper one the contents of a truck from Whitehill and Polton collieries are being tipped by a crane into a ship's hold. Below, a hold is being filled by a loading chute which could be directed to spread the load evenly. The coal has been brought to the dockside by the hopper trucks in the background.

The edge coals at Gilmerton lie almost vertical and for centuries people dug down into them. In the 1850s local coalmaster R.B.W. Ramsay was working them from day levels – shallow workings drained by adits (underground tunnels) into the North Esk. Small-scale operations continued intermittently until 1928 when the Fordell Mains (Midlothian) Colliery Co. sunk two shafts to work at deeper levels. The colliery was operated by the Gilmerton Colliery Company and, when the Coal Board took it over, no fewer than thirteen seams were being worked: the Little Splint, Five Foot, South Parrot, Flex, Great, Stairhead, Gillespie, Blackchapel, Peacocktail, Corbie, Peacock, Carlton and Blue.

The colliery's past caught up with it in November 1961. Over the years the old pits had been filled with agricultural waste and, like any good compost heap, the rotting vegetable matter generated heat. At some time it spontaneously combusted somewhere deep underground. It could have been burning for a long time before it crept into the workings. A fire burning out of control in near-vertical seams hundreds of feet high, with the pit acting like a huge lum, was the stuff of nightmares. The colliery was sealed and never reopened.

The Benhar Coal Company took its name from the East and West Benhar coal workings which straddled the Lanarkshire/West Lothian border near Harthill. It became the Niddrie and Benhar Coal Co. after 1882 when it took over the lease of Niddrie colliery which was worked at various depths from several shafts and inclines strung out along the outcrops. Niddrie closed in September 1927, but the brickworks, workshops, locomotive sheds and offices continued to service the neighbouring Woolmet and Newcraighall Collieries. These pugs are working the mineral line that linked them together.

The company gave up its interests at Benhar in 1897 and concentrated its efforts on Midlothian where it had just begun to develop a colliery at Newcraighall. The area had been heavily worked in the past, but the new workings extended the boundaries and went to deeper levels. A single vertical shaft was sunk to just over 800 feet to augment staged haulage inclines, or dooks. They extended for two miles and took the workings out beyond the Musselburgh foreshore. A huge new colliery that promised work and wages for over a hundred years was the Scottish miners' equivalent of striking gold – which is perhaps why they called it the Klondyke.

During the Second World War, a curious incident brought Newcraighall to a standstill. Coal was vital to industry, and miners were exempt from conscription. They faced certain obligations and in August 1943 when two Newcraighall men refused to go underground as instructed, they were regarded as having breached a National Service Order. They were sentenced at Edinburgh Sheriff Court to a month's imprisonment. A strike in support of them by 200 night-shift men escalated to include all 1,500 men at Newcraighall and Woolmet pits. Sending them all to prison would have been impractical (and silly) and an awkward situation was resolved by the men persuading their imprisoned colleagues to accept the original instruction.

A more serious incident in August 1953 threatened to halt production at Newcraighall again. Five men were cut off from the main road by a roof fall and trapped behind the debris for twelve hours. There was only one way into the area and no second means of escape, in contravention of the 1911 Coal Mines Act. The manager and under-manager were dismissed and an oversman and fireman demoted for three months. When the under-manager was re-employed, the union threatened a strike which was only averted when the Coal Board agreed to prosecute the sub-area production manager, agent, manager and under-manager.

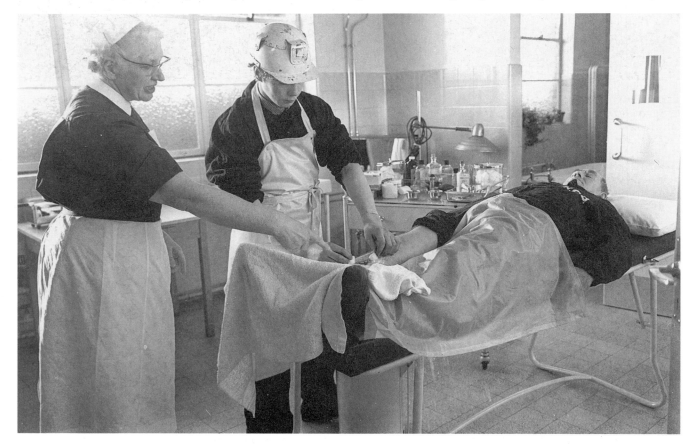

The big incidents tended to obscure the ordinary every-day hazards of mining. Pit-head baths usually had a first-aid room attached and in the early 1950s the Coal Board took the provision of medical services further by opening properly staffed medical centres to serve an area. Here at Newcraighall a nurse instructs a first-aid trainee, while above, a 'casualty' is taken from the pit-head in a rescue exercise.

This picture, from 1957, shows shot firers stemming shot-holes at Newcraighall. The man on the left is using his carbide lamp to illuminate the hole for his colleague. Carbide lamps were introduced in 1905 and were a great advance on the old tally lamps. They had containers of water and calcium carbide which when mixed gave off acetylene gas. It burned with a bright flame. Electric battery lamps were introduced in 1940, but it took a long time for miners to give up their old lamps. Newcraighall was unusual in that the undersea workings, known as the Sea Dook district, were classified as a flame safety area while the rest of the pit was worked with naked lights.

Newcraighall was put on to single shift working in 1962 and in 1965 was categorised as having a limited life. It was closed in 1968.

The little mining village of Newcraighall was expanded by the Niddrie and Benhar Company. They built rows of two-storeyed brick houses with dry outside toilets, outdoor pumps for water supplies and unpaved streets. The village was absorbed into Edinburgh by boundary changes in 1920 and five years later the Park View and Park Terrace houses were built. The village was degenerating into a slum by 1950 and with the closure of the colliery in 1968 it became the target for demolition. A fight by the tenants forced the council to change their plans and over the next twenty years Newcraighall village was progressively redeveloped.

Woolmet colliery was sunk between 1898 and 1904 by the Niddrie and Benhar Coal Co. Shaft sinking was a dangerous and uncomfortable job; it was also a very wet one. Sinkers wore wide brimmed hats and in the days when they relied on a tally lamp for light they protected the flame from falling water with a curved metal shield. These men at Woolmet may have been the sinking crew, or 'shanksmen' who maintained the shaft or shank.

This picture of the Woolmet headgear was taken in 1925. The colliery consisted of a single 735 foot shaft, an incline and a surface mine. The pit bottom was an enormous space, like an underground cathedral.

These pictures show two stages of the construction of the washer at Woolmet in the 1920s. The men erecting the reinforcing rods for the concrete washer cone in the lower picture look like flies caught in a giant spider's web. New baths were opened at the pit in February 1931.

Woolmet was classified as a category 'A' pit in 1962, but had dropped to category 'B' in 1965 and was closed in September the following year. The reasons for closure were given as difficult, uneconomic working conditions and approaching exhaustion, but such a rapid decline, coinciding with the opening of Monktonhall, was greeted with some cynicism by the miners. All of the displaced men went to work in Monktonhall.

The flash-lit pictures on these two pages (and the front cover) were taken at Woolmet in the early 1950s. In those days, like many other non-gassy pits, Woolmet was a 'naked light' pit – one in which men could use flame lamps, or smoke if they wanted to. Such practices were stopped following fatal disasters at Kames (Ayrshire) and Lindsay (Fife) collieries in the 1950s. The new regulations meant that anyone taking flammable materials – 'contraband' – down the pit could be immediately dismissed.

In words typical of the kind of casual humour miners applied to such dangerous looking situations, someone has chalked 'take me out' on these curved roof supports which have been contorted by the crushing movement of the roof. Ordinary mortals might wish to ignore the broken girder's proxy plea and quickly take themselves out of such a situation!

These men are drilling into a roof at Woolmet with a Burnside borer – the same piece of equipment seen in use at Westwood shale pit on page 38. The operation was intended to drain water from the upper levels of the pit to relieve pressure through the strata on the Monktonhall shaft which was being sunk nearby. When the drill broke through, the water was allowed to continue to flow and the force of it hitting the pavement was enough to bore a little hole of its own. As part of the same operation to take the pressure off the Monktonhall sinking a huge submersible pump was installed at the abandoned Niddrie No. 13 shaft.

The intention to sink a huge new pit in the area between Newcraighall, Woolmet, Carberry and Wallyford was announced in 1950. The exact location had not been chosen, but when the site at Millerhill was eventually fixed it was where this old miners' row, Adam's Row, once stood. The new pit was intended to work the deep Midlothian coals and was expected to be the country's first 'million tonner' (output of a million tons a year). Initial predictions that the pit would sustain this output for 100 years had been reduced to 50 years by the time the pit opened!

The first sod of Monktonhall colliery was cut on 16th December 1953. The ceremony was performed by Mrs R.B. Parker, wife of the NCB's finance director, who was handed the ceremonial spade by fifteen year old John Higginson on the right. He was the third generation of his family to work in the industry and the youngest employee at the neighbouring Woolmet colliery. On the left is the Rev. Eaton of Newton Parish Church who blessed the venture and in the centre, George Kirkwood, Lothians Area General Manager (whose picture as a young rescue brigadesman is on page 61).

Six weeks after the sod-cutting ceremony the collar for the first of two 24 foot diameter shafts was taking shape. In the background of this picture is Woolmet colliery which worked the coals above 1,000 feet, but Monktonhall was to go down another 2,000 – deeper than any pit had been sunk in Scotland. The wet and muddy field was only a minor foretaste of the discomforts the shaft sinkers were to encounter over the next seven years.

A large volume of water escaping from old flooded workings in the area poured into the first 1,100 feet of the shafts, and high capacity sinking pumps were needed to keep it under control. At deeper levels the difficulties increased. Natural water feeders shot into the shafts under such high pressure that special chemical sealants were needed to stem the flows. The heavy waterproof clothes and wide brimmed hats worn by these sinkers convey some sense of the wet, mucky and dangerous conditions they had to work in.

With the shafts complete, mine drivage and development work began early in the 1960s and the new showpiece pit was officially opened on 26th January 1965. The first section had been opened three weeks earlier and was already producing 600 tons of coal a day. This was expected to rise to 4,000 tons as the pit worked up to full capacity. Coal was brought to the surface in 15 ton skips in No. 1 shaft while men and materials were wound in No. 2. Double deck cages carried 144 men in a single wind and locomotive-hauled man-riding trains, operating on level roads, took the men to their working places. Face operations were fully mechanised. For the first ten years work was concentrated on the Great seam at 2,700 feet, although eleven other seams were expected to be worked, down to the North Greens seam at 3,630 feet.

Monktonhall had an assured market with the vast bulk of its output going to Cockenzie power station on a British Rail train operating system called 'Merry-go-round'. The coal, crushed to lumps of about an inch and stored in a bunker, could be loaded into 700 ton capacity trains in three minutes. The trains had continuous air brakes and ran at express passenger speeds.

By the end of 1969 the pit was reaching its peak. In November it broke the British record for weekly output from a single face with 13,305 tons and smashed it in December with 16,453 tons, believed to have been a European record. Twenty years later, Monktonhall was mothballed.

In June 1992 the pit was leased by a workers' co-operative. It eventually comprised 167 men who each sunk £10,000 into the venture in an attempt to revive their old industry. Older men put in redundancy money, but most were young men who borrowed from families or raised the cash at commercial rates. They were brave and the scale of what they took on can be gauged from this cathedral-like underground junction. They started in high spirits and happily worked long hours to make the shared venture a success. At its peak the co-operative produced 7,500 tons of coal a week and employed other miners to bring the workforce up to 300 men.

With every pit employing over 100 men legally bound to have a trained rescue team and, with no exemption clause in the Coal Mines Act for brave ventures, the worker's co-operative had to have a rescue team. They were trained at the Crossgates Rescue Station in Fife. There was one fatality in the co-operative's time in charge of the pit when a miner was killed by a roof fall in 1993.

The venture was undercapitalised and was soon in trouble. Debts rose, men worked for no wages and when the laundry contractor repossessed the overalls, they had to work in their own pit clothes. Wives had to wash them, and learn skills forgotten since the days before pit-head baths.

Private mining companies were invited to
take over and in 1994 Waverley Mining
Finance stepped in with a £7 million rescue
package. The original investors gave up their
10,000 shares for Waverley shares on
condition they couldn't sell them for three
years. Wages were cut. Against advice, a new
face, PC8, was opened in the Peacock seam –
so called because of the spectral highlights
on the surface of the coal. Water, already a
problem in the pit, started to pour in. The
entire Lothian coalfield was in effect
draining into the pit and the pumps could
not cope. In April 1997 Waverley Mining Finance bowed to the inevitable and called in the liquidator – an appropriate
title for someone who was to wind up the affairs of the flooded pit. Hopes were raised briefly in June when Caledonian
Mining showed an interest, but there was no saviour. No. 2 winding tower, seen here, was blown up in November 1997
and No. 1 was toppled in February 1998. The last deep mine in the Lothians, the NCB's showpiece, had gone.

SOME FURTHER READING

This is a selection of useful titles and not a comprehensive bibliography.

R.W. Dron, *The Coal Fields of Scotland*, 1902.
R. Page Arnott, *A History of the Scottish Miners*, 1955.
NCB, *A Short History of the Scottish Coal Mining Industry*, 1958.
Augustus Muir, *The Story of Shotts*, c.1952.
Alan Bridges (Editor), *Industrial Locomotives of Scotland*, 1976.
David Kerr, *Shale Oil: Scotland*, 1994.
Robert Lee and Robert McKenzie, *Fauldhouse Victoria Cricket Club*, 1991.
Andrew S. Cunningham, *Mining in Mid and East Lothian*, 1925.
George Dott, *Early Scottish Colliery Waggonways*, 1947.
M.J. Worling, *Early Railways of the Lothians*, 1991.
Andrew M. Hajducki, *The Haddington, Macmerry and Gifford Branch Lines*, 1994.

Also by Guthrie Hutton from Stenlake Publishing:
MINING: Ayrshire's Lost Industry, ISBN 1 872074 88 X.
Lanarkshire's MINING Legacy, ISBN 1 84033 015 5.

HELP!

As with my two previously published books on the mining industries of Ayrshire and Lanarkshire I have had some difficulty in gathering a comprehensive selection of pictures for this book. Inevitably there will be criticism of the poor coverage of some areas, but this is simply because the material is not available. The mining industry has never been pretty and the people associated with it were often too poor to afford a camera, so pictures of it are not abundant. If you have any that show any aspect of the industry, please don't throw them away – they could be a vital part of our nation's industrial heritage. Your local library or the Scottish Mining Museum at Newtongrange would be very pleased to receive them, or copy them if you don't want to part with them.

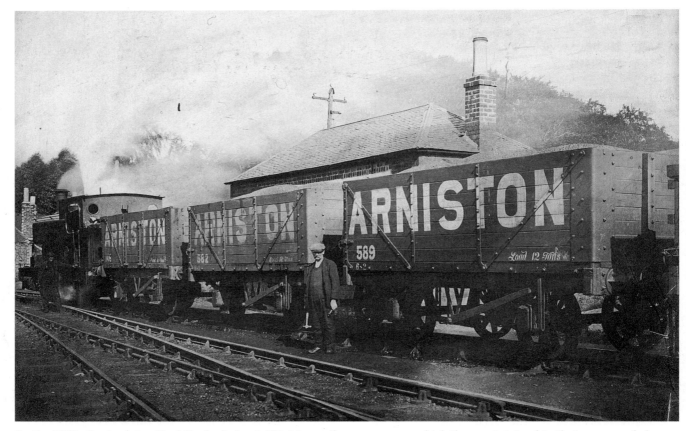

In the 1890s the Arniston Coal Co. had about 400, 8 ton railway waggons which they maintained in their own workshops. They also had three pugs for moving them around the colliery sidings.